THE QUANTUM BRAIN

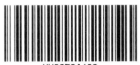

Also by Amit Goswami

The Self-Aware Universe
Science and Spirituality
The Visionary Window
Physics of the Soul
The Quantum Doctor
God Is Not Dead
Creative Evolution
How Quantum Activism Can Save Civilization Quantum Creativity
Quantum Economics
The Everything Answer Book
Quantum Politics

See the World as a Five Layered Cake
(With Sunita Pattani) Quantum Psychology and Science of Happiness

(With Carl Blake and Gary Stewart) Quantum Activation: Turning Obstacles into Opportunities

Also by Amit Goswami and Valentina R. Onisor

Quantum Spirituality

Upcoming books by Amit Goswami and Valentina R. Onisor

The Quantum Integrative Medicine
The Awakening of Intelligence
The Quantum Science of Love and Relationships

Goswami and Onisor once again drive a golden chariot across the millennial ridge, exiting 20th Century radical materialism for the illuminated "New Land" of a post-material, consciousness-based existence - **Prof. Lisa Miller, Columbia University**

THE QUANTUM BRAIN

Amit Goswami, PhD
Valentina R. Onisor, MD

Understand, Rewire and Optimize Your Brain

BlueRose Publishers

First Published in March 2021

ISBN: 978-93-5427-386-5

Price: INR 295/-

BLUEROSE PUBLISHERS

www.bluerosepublishers.com

info@bluerosepublishers.com

+91 8882 898 898

Cover Design:

Debabrata Dey Biswas

Typographic Design:

Deepika Matpal

Distributed by: BlueRose, Amazon, Flipkart, Shopclues

This book is dedicated to all brave explorers who are interested in taming brain's conditioned me-centeredness and negativity in order to rewire and optimize their brain for the exploration of infinite human quantum potentiality

PREFACE

A few years ago, I (Amit) appeared in a movie that has now become a New Age classic: *What the Bleep Do We Know?* In that movie, I said a line that touched a chord with many viewers: "Quantum physics is the physics of possibilities (for consciousness to choose from)." The movie presented the upbeat version of quantum physics via such statements as above that two physicists, Fred Alan Wolf and I made. The movie also presented a good deal of the phenomenon of neuroplasticity. Together, the science presented made a potent case that the combination quantum physics and neuroscience can be a powerful force for us to make lifestyle changes and can even help with drug addiction, which was part of the movie.

Ever since, I have been eager to put some effort in developing a quantum theory of neuroscience. Like the rest of biology, neuroscience right now is also based on the philosophical dogma of material monism— ''everything-is-matter''—and as such it is full of loopholes, conceptual gaps that are impossible to fill within the purview of that philosophy.

Meanwhile, the need for a quantum neuroscience is growing as more and more millennials become slaves of their brain, avid addicts of information-processing, dumbed down and oblivious of their infinite quantum potentiality.

Other important preoccupations have kept me busy all these years; but finally, I have managed to write the book on a theory of quantum neuroscience, originally envisioned in 2004-2005. The research that lead to the book revealed much brain data in support of the quantum science and quantum worldview that

I have been developing since my book *The Self-Aware Universe* was released in 1993. I present all that too.

My co-author, Valentina R. Onisor is a family physician, a long-time dedicated consciousness researcher and a pioneer in the rapidly developing field of Quantum Integrative Medicine and Quantum Education. She has a life-long interest in integrating the brain and the body functions and in that way optimizing the functions of both. We wrote the book *Quantum Spirituality* together as an exploration of "Wholeness", and she brings the same integrative spirit for the research that we report here.

This book is about the import of quantum neuroscience for interested readers struggling to make lifestyle changes toward more meaning, more purpose, more creativity, more love, more happiness, and more intelligence in their lives. This book is written stylistically for interested laypersons (but of course, it is intended for everybody) and the message is the same as that of the aforementioned movie except that it is presented with much more mature and coherent scientific back-up.

The new quantum science and the worldview that it gives us is optimistic as opposed to the old science which depicts us as programmed machines struggling to cope with negative emotional brain circuits and circuits of pleasure-addiction. In this new science, what we previously could not even talk about in scientific terms—our subjective experiences such as love, happiness, and spirituality—finds voice and explanation, and more. This new science gives us guidelines for improvement and enhancement of the workings of the brain. Dear reader, you will find that the quantum science of the brain and intelligence that we present here explains all the exalted states that people of wisdom tradition report; they are now finding support in the neuroscience data. I hope that inspires you as it does us. Can we transform? Can we take charge, use our creativity to rewire the brain, and optimize it to gain unlimited access to intelligence and act accordingly? Can you? Yes, we all can. We hope this book is of considerable help in that direction.

Special thanks to Prof. Atish Mozunder for a careful reading of the manuscript. We also thank our students at Quantum Activism Vishwalayam for their patient study of earlier manuscripts.

Thanks are also due to the editorial staff of Bluerose publishers.

TABLE OF CONTENTS

CHAPTER 1

You are More than Your Brain: The Relationship between Consciousness, Quantum Physics, and Your Brain

Today, most neuroscientists tell you that your brain is all that you are and the brain cannot change, more or less. They also tell you that your brain is a material machine, a cognizing computer of sorts. Then they debate about such things as the location of consciousness in your brain. Or what part of your brain's actions is unconscious and what is conscious. That's what researching consciousness means for them.

Are you more than your brain? You can be if your consciousness is beyond the brain. Brain scientists refute such proposals by accusing dualism. How can consciousness be a non-physical dual entity? If it were so, how does it interact with the material brain?

But now there is quantum physics which is giving us a revolutionary new track to think of consciousness and the brain. The quantum model of consciousness and the brain gives us predictions that avant-garde neuroscientists have verified in the laboratory. What happens to brain science when we look at consciousness as primary and the brain is quantum, not Newtonian and determined? This is the subject of this book.

Why is this important to you? Perhaps you are one of those people who are not happy with the idea of being a machine that cannot change. Because you know through your own experience that you can change; you have; you are not a machine.

You are not alone. Today, there are many people like you who are unhappy with the human condition most people live in: me-centeredness, negative emotional behaviors dominating them, pleasure-seeking that leads to addiction—these features are built into the brain. There are psychological and spiritual traditions that are available and following their lead anyone can make some changes in their lives, and hence live better. The psychological and spiritual techniques, however, are incomplete as are their explanations.

This all should make you curious: Does science have an explanation contrary to the ones mainstream neuroscientists provide?

The answer in this book is: yes. Quantum science has explanations:

1) Of why the brain behaves the way it does giving you that base-level human condition – me-centeredness, negative emotional brain circuits, pleasure and addiction;

2) Of why and how the psychological and spiritual techniques, old and new, work so that everyone can use them to improve the behavior of their brains.

And the best part of the book is this: now that we know how the brain came to what it is, now that quantum science gives us a verified scientific theory of how the brain works, we can build on the existing techniques of transformation and make it very comfortable for you to live with your brain and use such methods optimally for accomplishing your goals in life.

The key to understanding the brain is to understand consciousness and its relation to the brain. What is consciousness? Consciousness is a 'what?' that is hard to talk about. Think about it. What we talk about within our science that is developing for the past four centuries we call objects, things, stuff, entities. Is consciousness an object? Does it have a location? You say, why not if neuroscientists talk about consciousness as an object. But better be careful. These are scientists who believe in a dogma called material monism that every "what" we talk about is an object, in fact a material object. You know the saying, "If you have a hammer in your hand, you see the world as nails".

There is another saying that will set you straight. "What we are looking for is what is looking". Yes; *that* is the problem: consciousness is both the looker and the looked at; both the subject and the object of an experience. And scientists, who look at consciousness as only an object, miss the boat to begin with.

The problem is that no neuroscientist knows how to introduce a "subject" in traditional science, the tradition that the great Newton had created for us. Newton's science still dominates and sets the context and the worldview of most scientists and most science. And that includes most of psychology, – science of the psyche, our internal world, and virtually all of neuroscience – science of the neurons and the conglomerate they make, the brain.

Let's talk about psychology a bit. Modern psychology made an impact on all of us because of Freud's revolutionary work introducing the concept of the unconscious. What is unconscious? Unconscious is consciousness of which we are not aware. It is conscious awareness that brings about the quandary of a subject looking at objects, the subject-object split. The subject/self is the first person "I" that you and we all experience.

All kinds of questions crop up when we try to apply science to understand Freud. Is unconscious a separate domain of reality outside of our space-time-matter-motion world? Freud and his followers or 'depth psychologists' believe so. There is that question of dualism again. It is so difficult to explain it that scientists generally avoid talking about the unconscious.

Neuroscientists talk about unconscious brain actions, arousal of awareness and conscious brain actions. But without having a distinction between subject and object, without a distinction between unconscious and conscious, all this talk just boils down to sophistry, play of words to hide the real problem.

Go back to an earlier time, perhaps as early as seven thousand years, yes seven thousand years. Then in India, a bunch of people, Indian culture calls them *rishi*s (*rishi* is a Sanskrit word meaning sage) but I would call them the first scientists of consciousness studies, had a solution to the problem, sort of. Again, the problem is to distinguish between unconscious and conscious awareness. And these scientists of consciousness of the old proclaimed a solution: Consciousness, a Oneness, is reality, One and only. Creating an illusion to experience itself as separate from itself, it splits itself into two, a subject looking at object(s).

"Why should the Oneness do that, split itself that is?" you ask, as many people before you have asked. The traditional answer was, "It is a play". Later the Oneness came to be known as God; and then the manifest world where subjects look at objects separate from themselves was called God's play in the playground that the world is.

These initial explorers of consciousness sang the glory of both the creator (Oneness) and the created (the world of separateness). But their followers misunderstood. If the world is created via an illusion, why bother about the world?

You may have seen the movie *Matrix* where a villain manipulates you via programs in your head from outside or the TV show *Star Trek: The Next Generation* where the idea of a holodeck appears—the apparently human play in the world could be a play of holographic images in a holographically projected world, couldn't it? The notion of a being creating the world by illusion sure sounds like these later ideas where more modern terms are used: programmer and programs. No wonder modern scientists call those original researchers of consciousness Mystics.

But of course, the way the followers of the original researchers interpreted their *gurus* was plain wrong; they did not think adroitly. The world we play in has order, cause and effect; and purpose: the orderly part of the world evolves producing more and more order. And the evolution is all lawful and purposeful. Illusions don't exhibit order that lasts and keeps growing for billions of years.

Quantum Physics

The scientific breakthrough for thinking about consciousness came as a big surprise that all creative breakthroughs are accompanied with quantum physics, a new physics that has replaced the old Newtonian physics for almost a century and supports the Indian *rishis*' solution that our subject-object duality comes from Oneness. The understanding came in stages:

1. Possibility nature of objects: It was recognized that quantum objects are waves of possibility; only when measured, they become particles of actuality;

2. Non-locality: When two possibility waves interact locally, that is, coming close together, they become correlated or entangled. What this means is radical: these correlated objects communicate instantly, without requiring signals. Why is this radical? Because Einstein's theory of relativity shows that in space and time all objects can interact or communicate

only via signals that move only with a finite speed for which the limit is the speed of light. Instant communication is called non-local;

3. The measurement problem: Since all material objects, both micro and macro, are quantum objects of possibility in principle (though we recognize that at the macro-level the behavior approaches Newtonian), what defines a measurement? There is a mathematical theorem, von Neuman's theorem, which says that no material interaction can convert a possibility wave into actuality. A non-material agency is required.

When we measure a quantum object like an electron, we use a measurement apparatus like a photographic film or a bunch of Geiger counters. Von Neuman's theorem makes them all impotent to do their job! Perhaps the only exception is the observer if we grant that he has nonmaterial consciousness. Thus, we arrive at the big question of measurement: Does observer's consciousness collapse or convert quantum waves of possibility into particles of actuality?

4. The paradox of observer's friend: But then a paradox also arises –suppose the observer's friend measures the electron at the same time as the observer. A possibility wave of an electron exists in many possible positions all at the same time (like all waves do); the collapse must consist of consciousness choosing one of these possible positions into actuality. Now suppose the friend chooses a different position than our observer. Whose choice counts? No reasonable criterion exists to discern why one observer's choice should count more than another's. And obviously,

both observers' choice cannot manifest for the same localized event.

In 1985, in a flash of creative insight about the meaning of quantum physics, I (Amit) was able to comprehend the explanation of all of these puzzles:

1. Quantum waves of possibility reside in a domain outside space and time; let's call it the domain of potentiality;
2. Any two objects in the domain of potentiality can correlate and communicate instantly. Instant communication means oneness since you can only communicate with yourself instantly. In this way, the domain of potentiality is a domain of potential Oneness. This Oneness is consciousness.
3. Measurement happens when this One consciousness chooses one actuality out of the many-faceted possibility wave. In the process, consciousness identifies with the observer's manifest brain and becomes a subject looking at the object, the manifest electron at a specific position on a photographic film or at one Geiger counter out of the whole bunch.
4. There is no paradox of the observer's friend because the choosing consciousness is one, the same for every observer.

This explains all the puzzles: split of the Oneness into subject and object, the role of the brain, even how to distinguish between unconscious and conscious. Unconscious is the Unmanifest or the Oneness; conscious is the space and time reality with subject-object split awareness . In effect, all those unresolved questions, unresolved for millennia, unresolved even after four hundred years of modern science are now solved.

Accordingly, I wrote a book, *The Self-Aware Universe: How Consciousness Creates the Material World*, elucidating how the Oneness, Consciousness, creates and experiences the material world through us. Quantum physics is the physics of possibilities; additionally, it is also a physics of us subjects who experience the possibilities as they manifest. To repeat, my insight was that material quantum possibilities are consciousness' own possibilities to choose from; as consciousness chooses, it splits into the experiencer subject (us) and the experienced material world.

So, we have to extend the scope of our physics beyond Newton's version to quantum physics in order to include both the unconscious Oneness and the conscious awareness of subject-object split separateness. And then, the illusion we spoke of above that the *rishi*s theorized, does not sound mystical and somebody's whimsy – oppressive - anymore but perfectly logical, purposive, and scientific. Furthermore, we, the human subjects of experience, experience the objects of the world via the brain. Mystical thinking never explained the role of the brain; this is why I said when talking about these *rishi*s' work that they had a "sort of" solution of dualism. The new science does explain what the mystics could not, the important role of the brain.

Quantum Neuroscience

All good and settled? Not quite. Most scientists had already bought the dogma of material monism, all-is-matter philosophy, lock, stock and barrel; they are not ready to accept the primacy of consciousness. Fortunately, experimental scientists are not too much into philosophical dogma; they do their experiments whenever the technology is available. It is the neuroscientists and their new technologies applied to brain research that are giving revolutionary support not only to my original breakthrough work, but all the subsequent research Valentina and I have done for this book.

So here it is: a complete neuroscience of our consciousness and the varieties of our experiences. What is in the book that is useful for you the nonscientist seeker of who you are and how to be happy, in spite of the foibles of your brain, beyond what you can find in other books on the brain including my earlier books? Let *us* count the ways:

- Does quantum physics apply to your everyday life? A related scientific question is: Can the brain, being a macro-object, develop macroscopic quantum possibilities for consciousness to choose from?

The answers? The first is a question that materialists ask mostly as a decoy to quench your enthusiasm about the meaning of quantum physics. Of course it applies to your everyday life. Quantum physics is the physics of possibilities. As I pointed out in my very first book on the subject, *The Self-Aware Universe*, to use quantum physics in a paradox-free way scientists have to postulate an agent of causation that converts possibility into actuality (call it downward causation of conscious choice), and that agent has to be a Oneness (quantum physics and experimental data demands it) that splits into a subject and an object in a quantum measurement. In other words, the Oneness, the causal agent of downward causation, is what we call consciousness. This one discovery sets the ground for the integration of science and spirituality, no less. If spirituality is important to you, so is quantum neuroscience because it gives evidence of your spirituality.

The second question is well taken. Macro-objects at room temperature are known to be notoriously Newtonian, and the brain should not be an exception. There are some speculative theories about a quantum brain that the scientific materialist gleefully refutes.

In this book, we give a definitive explanation of how consciousness can connect with the brain even though the material brain is approximately Newtonian. It is via non-physical quantum organizing fields behind our feelings and thoughts that consciousness connects to the brain, in fact to all living beings. Our feelings and thoughts are quantum movements. Their quantum connections give the brain its non-Newtonian quantum features.

- Spiritual traditions and more recently transpersonal psychology posit that we have two modalities of the self that arise in connection with the brain. In my earlier work, I have developed the quantum science of the two-self modality – the quantum self and the ego. In this book, we will go through the whole thing again but in conjunction with the resolution of what cognitive neuroscientists call the paradox of perception. The new science is an integrative science: not only does it integrate science and spirituality, but also quantum physics and cognitive neuroscience. We will further show that neuroscience data has confirmed this idea of two selves, additionally giving us definitive data of a preconscious zone between the two modes that the theory predicts.

Why is this important to you? If you go to any advice *guru*, be it a spiritual teacher or a transpersonal psychologist, and talk about transformation, she will say, "Meditate". The concept of two selves with the bridge of preconscious between them explains many of our meditative spiritual experiences establishing the scientific validity of the efficacy of meditation to produce expansive states of consciousness. The brains of most people are conditioned to be constricted during most of their waking hours. Meditation is meant to train the brain to stay conducive to expansion of consciousness.

- Besides being a vehicle for consciousness to express itself as a subject or self, the brain is also known for its ability to make representations of the mind or mental thoughts that we call memory. There are many unexplained facts about memory, for example, memory retrieval; all these facts are explained in this book. We also explain the origin of our me-centeredness and personality.

If you are interested in transformation, you already are aware that one of the things you want to change is your excessive me-centeredness and inauthentic personalities you carry that keeps you from engaging in genuine relationships. The knowledge generated here is crucial for your effort.

- Our brain has negative emotional brain circuits accounting for much of the emotional turmoil that we create and suffer from. Evolutionary biologists tell us that they came from animal instincts, but give us no real theory. We will give you a complete theory and explanation.

Obviously, a theory of these negative emotional brain circuits will help you to look for and appreciate and explore the remedy when you see it in this book.

- We discuss the subject of pleasure and pleasure-centeredness and explain the differences between the experience of pleasure and that of happiness and how pleasure need not be negated, how pleasure can be used to enhance happiness.

You know, traditional spirituality is rather negative on pleasure. Surely setting a scientific perspective will help you to find a proper place for both pleasure and happiness in your life. In other words, quantum science tells us pleasure with moderation is not only okay but also necessary.

- We present data in support of the idea of reincarnation which is revolutionizing our concepts of the psychology of transformation.

The brain data will remove any doubts you harbor about the scientific validity of reincarnation. This will facilitate your exploration of meaning and purpose.

- A recent famous discovery of neuroscience is neuroplasticity; brain can change and we can affect its change. In this book, we will discuss how you can rewire your brain to improve the quality of your life using quantum principles of transformation. The Scottish actor Brian Cox expressed a widespread concern when he said in a recent interview, "The human condition essentially is quite a tragic condition." Literally, quantum science will show you the way out of this base level "tragic" human condition (me-centeredness, propensity for emotional negativity, pleasure-centeredness, information addiction) to higher levels of happiness.

This undoubtedly is the most important thing about the brain that you are looking for, ever since you became interested in transformation, be it for healing from addiction, be it for improving relationships, be it for positive mental health, be it for achieving abundance, including material abundance, be it for spiritual transformation. There are several brain books written on the subject, but frankly they are all compromised because they adhere to material monism.

- Using ideas of quantum creativity, and applying those ideas to the purely quantum energies (vital energy) that we feel, quantum science shows you how to optimize your brain's use via coordinating it with other body organs and awakening its latent capacities.
- Is there a "heart," a self at the heart that can occasionally overrule the brain's thinking self as mystics and many women claim? In this book, we will show that the answer from the perspective of quantum science is a very important 'yes'.
- Yes, this new science of the heart and the brain's relation to the heart is very important for people who explore love and desire personal growth and transformation that opens the door for unconditional love.
- The new knowledge will enable you to integrate your head and your heart.
- It may be possible to optimize our control of the brain to the extent of even subjugating those negative emotional brain circuits.

Convinced that this book has something important to tell you? We sure hope so. We also hope that you regard this book as a brain-owner's manual which not only tells you about maintenance but also about improvements. Hope you will follow through the suggested improvements and find satisfying transformation in your life. To this end, all the chapters have things for you to do. Bon voyage!

Newton's physics had been replaced by the new quantum physics almost a century ago. Quantum physics was discovered when we began to study the sub-microscopic scale of matter and energy as a series of surprises.

Surprise #1: We found that matter and energy are both made of elementary particles – grains that cannot be broken down further – except that the elementary particles of energy are called quanta (plural of quantum). Why is this a surprise? Everybody expected energy to be continuous, not grainy.

And then came the even bigger surprise #2: These quantum objects – elementary "particles" of matter and energy – are really waves although when we see them, they change into particles. Why is this surprising? Particles stay in one place at a time, even while moving they follow a well-defined trajectory. But waves spread out; they can be in more than one place at a time. For example, the crest lines of water waves go on expanding. What? The objects that we all still call elementary particles their true nature is wave?

But of course, surprise #3 explains: The waves are unusual; they are waves of possibility. We never see them in space and time; whenever we measure, the waves change into particles, a change that physicists call collapse. Why call it collapse? Initially, the researchers thought that the waves do their waving *in* space and time and when measured they really collapse a little at a time like a collapsible umbrella. But soon, the mistake was corrected: the collapse is instantaneous.

Realize this: Nothing moves instantaneously in space and time, where, objects have a speed limit that Einstein established as the speed of light. So, the waves are *unusual* waves of possibility, objects of many facets, residing in a domain outside space and time; let's call it the domain of potentiality. The multifaceted waves of possibility instantly become one-facetted objects or particles, when we measure.

For example, an electron is a wave of many possible positions all at the same time. When we measure, we find the electron only in one position, exhibiting a particle-like behavior.

Biggest surprise #4: The famous Einstein and two collaborators, Nathan Rosen and Boris Podolsky discovered that in the domain of potentiality, two waves of potentiality, simply by coming close and interacting, can be so "correlated" that they communicate instantly even when they move far apart. This should be verifiable experimentally if we measure two such correlated objects at a distance from each other. Do they communicate instantly at a distance, without signals? Yes, they do.

This important experimental verification was provided by the physicist Alain Aspect and his collaborators [Circa 1982].

Why is this last item worldview changing? Before Aspect's experiment, the domain of potentiality outside space and time was just a theory, something quantum physics predicted. But quantum physics could be wrong or incomplete. However, later on, quantum physics was proven to be the correct and a complete theory of physics and more. The domain of potentiality became fact. And what an amazing fact it is! Think. All objects in the domain of potentiality, if correlated, can communicate instantly. What does that mean? One can only communicate with oneself instantly, isn't it? So, all objects in the domain of potentiality are potentially one. The domain of potentiality is a domain of potential Oneness.

You see how close to truth the *rishis* in India seven thousand years ago came in postulating Oneness as the deeper reality from which separateness of the world of our experience arises. They did it from direct experience, their creative insight.

How do we know that the Oneness is consciousness? When we observe quantum objects in space and time, the objects actualize in the form of quanta or elementary particles. In this way, another big surprise. Somehow, we, the observers and the subject pole of experiences, are in the picture of the physics of elementary particles, quanta.

This is no surprise to you, if you already are a quantum aficionado. This is the famous quantum measurement problem, also called the observer effect. Trying to solve it with the prejudiced philosophy of materialist science – material monism – gives paradoxes of famous intriguing names such as the paradox of Schrodinger's cat, the paradox of Wigner's friend, the 'watched pot never boils' paradox, and so forth.

But paradoxes do get solved, only that you have to give up some prejudices. Darwin gave us a much-touted theory of evolution, but he had to give up his Christian prejudice of how God created all life in mere six days. Einstein discovered his theory of relativity, but he had to give up the age-old prejudice, time is absolute, time is independent of movement.

I (Amit) found the solution to the quantum measurement problem when in a sudden flash of creativity, I could give up the prejudice of material monism in favor of the idea that consciousness does matter into experiencing subjects and experienced objects. Succinctly put, my insight was this: consciousness is the ground of all being in which matter exists as multifaceted possibility waves; some of these possibilities belong to the object to be observed and others belong to the observer; but all these are possibilities of consciousness itself which become actualized as localized objects when consciousness chooses one of their facets out of many. In the process, consciousness identifies with the manifest brain of the observer and experiences itself as a subject separate from the object. In this way, the observer's brain gets an experiencing self.

This paradox-free interpretation (more details in chapter 3) of quantum physics and its measurement problem identifies the domain of potentiality as our Oneness consciousness, also asserting it as the very foundation of everything, all our experiences. Crucial to this way of thinking is the experimental revelation that the domain of potentiality is characterized by the possibility of signal-less communication or what we can call direct communication without the exchange of signals. In contrast, all communication in the domain of space and time has to use signals. Signals are *local* with a speed limit; what this means is that they go through space a little at a time with a finite speed. In contrast, we call signal-less instant communication *non-local.*

Thus, underlying the domain of potentiality is consciousness characterized by this non-locality, instant interconnection, Oneness. To repeat, all objects are potentially one in consciousness. Consciousness is one and undivided. It becomes separated as subject and object via quantum measurement.

However, the theory that I discovered for the brain's self says that since it is a representation of non-local consciousness, it too must be non-local, cosmic, a self that points to the unity. This gives a cognitive dissonance with the self-experience of most scientists, perhaps most people. Most individuals experience a very local self-identity most of the time, a constricted consciousness that we call ego or 'me', not the nonlocal expansive self of quantum measurement that I call the quantum self or simply "I."

How does the ego arise? From the get-go, I was quite aware of this problem too, and invoked the well-known mechanism of conditioning to solve it. Quantum measurement produces memory; reflection in the mirror of memory produces conditioning, tendencies to act that we call our habit patterns and character traits; the use of our ability to revisit our memories again and again and reconstructing them gives us personalized programs that constitute our personality. In this way, we get a second pole of the self-experience that I call ego-character-persona, I/me or simply "me," since the "I" tend to become implicit in this state.

Why is this important? There is the important follow-up question from every owner of the two-self polarity, the question of optimizing the self-experience. Your experiencing self is your "front" for your relationship with the world. If you know how to optimize the functioning of your experiencing self, you will be better in your relationship with the world.

And then there are other questions too. Do you, as a self, have the power to create, to manifest things? Do you have freedom or free will to initiate changes? These are questions about you and the two polarities of your experiencing self; but undeniably these are also questions about your brain's operation. Thinking of yourself as a brainless disembodied being, as some transpersonal psychologists tend to do, does not go very far, does it? Nor does it bid well to ignore the quantum self as the materialist scientists do; it is so easy to experience the expansion the quantum self brings to the average experience over a time (and the expansion is experienced as happiness) even when you are not fully aware of it. When you are fully in it, with awareness, even though only for a moment, you have *Samadhi* (a Sanskrit word), or *Satori* (a Japanese word), or *Ein Sof* (a Hebrew word) experience, or a Holy Spirit experience (as Christianity calls it), or you have a peak experience in more modern terms of transpersonal psychology. Make no mistake; every tradition is talking about the same experience. Many people have them.

Today, we have definitive brain data. It supports the idea of the quantum brain; it supports the quantum-self experience; it supports the explanation of the two-self polarity.

The Varieties of Human experiences

Spiritual traditions like the Indian Vedanta and Jewish Kabbala say that we, humans have four kinds of basic experiences of objects: sensing (of material objects), feeling (energies associated with living called vital energy), thinking (meaning and information), and intuition (of higher contexts of knowledge in terms of feeling and meaning). These higher contexts of knowledge we call archetypes: love, beauty, and truth are examples.

Quantum science further elaborates. Living requires purposive software programs that are associated with the physiological functions of the various organs of our body. Since material interactions are causal forces (they are initial cause of a change) and *not* purposive (think of purpose as a final cause), these programs are not the result of material cause. Consciousness, however, can choose with purpose, have a final cause in its intention behind the choice. For living organisms, the software programs that living requires are produced by consciousness using vital organizing fields as blueprints. Vital energies that we feel are the movements of these blueprints. I (Valentina) have become familiar with these movements first of all from my yoga study, later on from the traditional medicine wisdom and health practice.

Rupert Sheldrake first theorized these organizing blueprints and called them morphogenetic fields. The name morphogenetic refers to form, but the fields are more about organ function; so, we rename these fields more appropriately as liturgical fields; liturgy in Greek means function. Consciousness, using the liturgical/morphogenetic fields purposively programs the organ's function. It is the energy associated with the quantum movement of these liturgical/morphogenetic fields that we feel – vital energy. These energies have been known since millennia; Indians call them *prana*, the Chinese *chi*, the Japanese *ki*.

You may not even be familiar with pure feelings connected with the body organs. Feelings in the brain are always accompanied by thoughts; we call them emotions.

For organisms with a neocortex, there is additional software that consciousness makes and uses – software for processing meaning. Mental objects fundamentally are objects of meaning and thinking about them is subjective. We can take other people's meanings which have been socially agreed upon and represent them as objective symbols; meaning understood in this mechanical way is called information.

It is rather unfortunate that emotions and information are more familiar experiences for today's youth than pure feelings and original meanings leading to much misunderstanding about our available potentialities.

Intuition in the current culture is even more misunderstood. Many people equate intuition with a learned guess from a vast repertoire of past experiences as in a chess grandmaster's moves in a chess game. This is how materialists spread misinformation. This is not it.

You see a flower; this flower is beautiful. Is the beauty an inherent material property of the flower? No. When you are able to take a fresh look at it, the sight of the flower evokes in you an expansion of consciousness; consciousness responds with an archetypal intuition; your mind gives meaning to the archetypal response, convention names the meaning beauty, and that's how your thought comes, this flower is beautiful.

It is not necessary to have a physical stimulus to get an archetypal response either. In general, archetypes and intuitions are used by consciousness for creating elevated mental and vital software in human beings. They are summons from consciousness, a reminder to us of its wholeness and Oneness.

Connoisseurs know that intuitions are mere glimpses at the archetypes; they are the beginning of what can be a creative exploration of the archetypes to discover their suchness. As the philosopher Immanuel Kant correctly argued, rational thinking does not let us experience the archetypes in suchness. But post-Kantian researchers have discovered the creative process, quantum science has explained the process, and it is now scientific to claim that the creative exploration of an archetype leads to experiencing it in suchness. However, the brain does not have the capacity to make direct memory of archetypes; this is why we are stuck with making only representations of the archetypal insight with pure feelings and original meanings.

As a result, intuitions come to most of us commonly as intuitive thoughts. This causes confusion: how can you tell an intuitive thought from a rational thought? Fortunately, quantum science is here to resolve all these confusions concerning our various experiences. Intuitive thought does not follow logically from previous thought; there is a discontinuity, says quantum science.

Quantum science asserts that all four of our experiences come from potentialities. They are all potentialities of consciousness to choose from.

We will share with you the most important motivation for writing this book. Neuroscientists talk about the problem of the experiencing self as the hard problem, but there is one other hard problem: how to explain the large variety of experiences; experiences of meaning, experience of feelings and positive emotions in the body, experiences of expanded consciousness, experiences of intuition that bring archetypal values to us, experiences of 'Aha!' or surprise of creative insight, experiences of joy that athletes, artists, musicians, and poets call flow, experiences called *samadhi* mentioned above. These experiences are the doorways to higher intelligence and happiness. In our life, both of us have experienced most of these but we had to work hard, there was no beaten path. We wanted to give people the know-how: how to change the brain so everyone has a beaten path to these experiences; everyone has a chance to access the higher intelligence.

To conclude: In this book, we not only present a theory of the brain's self but also a theory of how the brain, a three-pound heap of molecules, gets its capacity to process meaning, feelings and emotions, intuitions and insights, expanded consciousness, flow and *samadhi*. In short, we now really have a comprehensive theory of the functioning of the whole brain and the means to improve and optimize the brain's functions. It is only now that a proper brain science has begun. This book will hopefully not only satisfy your curiosity, but also help you learn some brain science that you can use to explore the further reaches of intelligence and happiness.

The mysteries of consciousness and the mysteries of the brain
Both lay hidden in the night
God said, "Here's quantum Science,"
And there came morning and light.
(Thanks to Alexander Pope)

Experimental neuroscience has exploded in the last few decades; there are now lots and lots of data. However, much of it is just confirming the functions of the various parts of the neuroanatomy, just details. Some details you likely know are as follows:

- The brain is three pounds of folded tissue consisting of 1.1 trillion cells of which neurons (grey matter) amount to 100 billion, and the rest are supporting glia (mostly white matter).
- Neurons communicate with other neurons through synapses; on the average a neuron has about 5000 synapses. In other words, neurons form a complex network of many circuits and connections.
- At a receiving synapse, a neuron gets information-carrying signals from its neighbors in the form of molecules called neurotransmitters of which there are four important ones: dopamine, serotonin, norepinephrine and acetylcholine. These neurotransmitters are connected to our moods. For example, dopamine is associated with the pleasure-full mood.
- There are also other important brain molecules called neuropeptides the most famous of which is the opioid molecule called endorphin, famous for being responsible for what is called the runner's high. But it's not only the runner's high; endorphins are also responsible for the pleasure you get from eating hot chilies.

- The neuronal networks are divided into many areas giving us the details of neuroanatomy. There are two common ways for depicting the brain areas. The first is in the form of the various lobes (fig. 1a); the second is in the form of a triune brain of three concentric shells (fig. 1b).

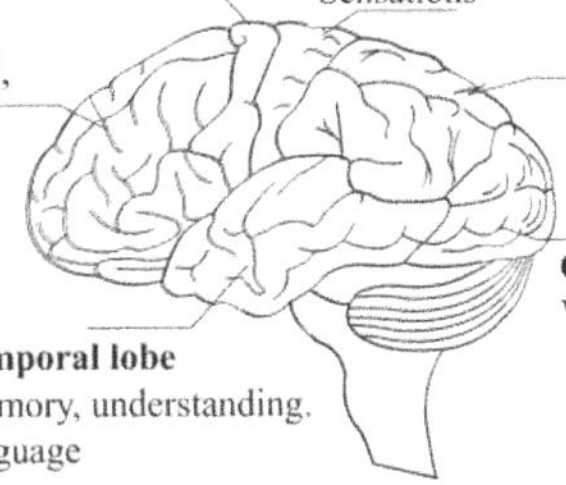

Figure 1a. Neuroanatomy: the lobes

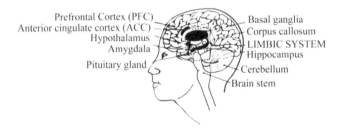

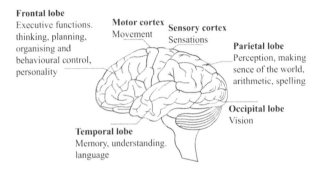

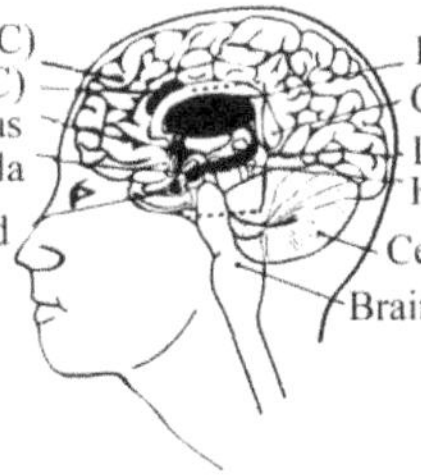

Figure1b. Neuroanatomy: the 3-part brain

- The neocortex or simply cortex is where the brain's ego or self-identity comes about and along with it, ego's decision-making. The neocortex is also the area where rational thinking takes place.

- The mid-brain is where the negative emotional and pleasure circuits of the brain are located.

There is other interesting data too, and some of them are anomalous from the perspective of Newtonian physics and the worldview of material monism. It is this anomalous data that is changing the attitude of the younger generation of neuroscientists that is coming along and taking leadership.

Let's consider the details of one of the most striking anomalous data alluded above. The data shows that when we do an ordinary conscious task such as thinking, the brain works in a very localized way, as expected. Only a few task-related areas are involved and the brain fluctuates between that and a default area which can be associated as its vegetative area of operation that the brain scientists call the self-agency area. But here is the surprise; this localized functioning is not all that happens. The brain also functions, and quite regularly, in a very synchronous way where many brain areas often distant from one another become involved. Such synchrony is impossible to establish through local communication via signals through neurons and glia. Newtonian physics and material interactions can only explain local functioning, not this apparently signal-less (non-local) functioning across distance. What binds together these different areas to act so synchronously except nonlocality?

To explain all of this, the two-self model of quantum science and transpersonal psychology is required. A quantum self that acts non-locally across much of the brain and a very localized self, your familiar ego.

Left Brain, Right Brain

In the nineteen eighties, there was a lot of hype about the hemispheric dichotomy of the brain: most brain apparatuses have a duplicate, they appear in both the left hemisphere and the right hemisphere of the brain. The hype was based on the fact that the left brain is analytical, while the right brain is holistic in its functioning. Of course, this does not make any difference in a normal brain because the two hemispheres are connected by a big bundle of nerve called corpus callosum. In epilepsy patients, the corpus callosum is discarded, which makes some significant difference. The most important one is that our conscious awareness is in the left brain; the right brain remains unconscious. The curious question is: Why is holistic right-brain processing left unconscious in us, whereas the analytic left-brain processing is conscious? Why is it not the other way around?

However, don't make a big case for any of it. If the left brain is damaged and is surgically removed, the right brain takes right over the self-awareness function. Does the brain's operation change from analytic to holistic in the process? The scanty data gives us no definitive answer.

There are many reasons that all this quantum and brain talk is important to you, the non-scientist reader. For one thing, the quantum science of the brain has put to rest some of the confusing assumptions that spiritual/religious traditions make. For example, according to the spiritual worldview, human beings are fundamentally all one; this oneness of everyone is a given and it is also a given that this Oneness is good and intelligent. The new science tells us a much less idealistic but much more pragmatic message given all the violence of human history: the Oneness is in potentiality and so are all its goodness and intelligence. Every human being can actualize his or her own Oneness or Oneness with another human being by simple means like intention, meditation, and loving friendship (call it entanglement or correlation); but until then separateness is operative. This is why goodness and intelligence do not always prevail. To think otherwise is not scientific.

So, the message of the new science to us is this: the human condition the average human being settles into via the intermediary of the brain is full of separateness-producing tendencies. The dark clouds of mental conditioning via the brain's memory making capacity do cover the sun of consciousness and its creative intelligence. 1) We develop the simple hierarchical ego much like the CPU of a computer. 2) We use our brains as computers; brain memory of the mind is a symbolic representation of mental meaning as objective information. These ordinary aspects of the human condition fit quite well with the materialist model and expectations and this is the reason that so many neuroscientists are fooled to vouch for it despite the problems with the hard questions and anomalies.

Here is the good news and why this new science is useful for you. In the new science, the dark clouds are only half the story. The other half is about the silver linings of the dark clouds. Human beings have infinite potentiality that they can explore through their intuitive and creative capacity to make changes and improve their condition and transform toward increasing intelligence (and increasing health and happiness); this involves much rewiring of the brain, coordinating the brain and the body, and some optimization of the functions of some of the body's and brain's organs.

The quantum worldview gives a theory of the means of achieving transformation in the form of a theory of human intuition and creativity; new data of neuroscience complements the means by demonstrating brain's neuroplasticity. The brain is not fixed in its adult memory once we reach adulthood as it was once thought.

Yes, when the clouds cover the sun, the predictions of the quantum paradigm match those of the materialist approach; in science this is called the correspondence principle. Under some conditions, the new paradigm becomes similar to the old. But remove those separateness producing conditions by which the brain rules you, and the new paradigm will show you its power by providing you the means to change your human condition toward the desired one, even an optimal one in which you use the brain for exploring new potentialities and self-renewal.

The journey toward the quantum self is a journey of increasing intelligence (and of increasing health and happiness), as you will see. In case you are wondering why, realize this: the quantum self is the doorway to an expanded consciousness of infinite new potentialities. The Sanskrit word for joy is *ananda*; it comes from another Sanskrit word *ananta*, meaning boundless. The words, 'happiness' and 'wholeness', have their roots in the same Greek word. Both words 'boundless' and 'wholeness' refer to expanded consciousness. *Happiness is expanded consciousness*. Although we humans desire both pleasure and happiness, the two are qualitatively different.

Developing the ability to choose the happiness of expansion of consciousness over the happiness gained from pleasure (that often contracts consciousness) is what awakening intelligence is all about.

We will give you an example. Many people today find sexual orgasms as their happiest experience. If you are one of these people and are a man, watch yourself next time when you are in the throw of a sexual orgasm. The very pleasurable male orgasm itself is very focused and localized, although short - when it is experienced with discharge (ejaculation), which is usually the case. However, you have to watch the aftermath. If you can avoid the usual male tendency of falling asleep you will find there is an afterglow due to a slight expansion of your consciousness. And *that* is part of the happiness as wholeness. For women, the clitoral orgasm is also quite focused and the same comment applies. It is an intense pleasure, although a superficial orgasm, that passes (and it can make you narcissist, if this is all you do). But if you are one of those fortunate women who are in a polar love relationship with a suited partner and are already G-spot sensitive, that is, you have awakened your sensuality, you can experience the expansion of consciousness and happiness during love-making almost right away (the G spot orgasm is a deeper form of orgasm).

Of course, things are much more complex than this, and will be discussed in a future book. But - is there a connection between your sexual energy, love and the life quality or even brain potentiality? You bet! Most people that I (Valentina) have met suffer from lack of integration in these areas, which reflects in all their life and actions.

Similarly, there is satisfaction in the use of the rational mind when you accomplish an objective, but without passion where is the motivation, where is the juice, the energy? For human beings in the base-level human condition, the motivation comes from the brain's supposedly unconscious memory of negative emotions such as competitiveness and domination and witness the mayhem that creates. Processing old memory to deduce new results in a machine-like way does not improve the situation much either. But once you engage the passion of curiosity, your intuition awakens, the quantum self comes into action, and you may get significant results. When inspiration and passion of curiosity (part of what we call emotional intelligence) join rationality, mental intelligence becomes creative intelligence.

But it takes more than the bossy brain to opt for *ananda* rather than pleasure, real intelligence rather than machine intelligence. If you choose to explore increasing levels of intelligence, you will also be exploring increasing levels of happiness or *ananda*. So, what will it be for you?

There is story from seventeenth-century India which I will modify slightly, modernize it a bit. A mighty king likes battles and conquering. His biggest desire is to fight the king before him who had built an empire even bigger. "If I can defeat him in battle, then I will prove myself to be the greatest." So, he looks for the old king and finds him. The guy is sitting under a tree.

"What are you doing?" the king asked.

"I am meditating," the other king answered.

"Get up. I want to fight with you," the king ordered. The other guy watched him and did nothing.

"Answer me!" the king was enraged.

The old king said, "I am a renunciate. I am old now and tired of fighting with my old and forever enemy. Why battle me? Why don't you battle him?"

The king was curious, "Who is this enemy of yours?"

"When I discovered how unruly and bossy this enemy is, I concentrated on conquering it rather than my other enemies who were no challenge in comparison. I gave up my kingdom and started fighting this enemy full time."

"Tell me who it is. I will beat him," said our king.

"It is my brain. Your biggest enemy is your brain. It is constantly throwing unwanted thoughts and emotions at you. Fight your brain and subdue it. If you can, only then I will fight you. Else you give up your empire and join me."

The king thought nothing of it and tried to tame his brain. But of course, he couldn't. And finally, he too gave up and becomes a renunciate.

In the olden days, people did not know how the brain works and could not tame it. Today's neuroscientists don't understand the brain either but they don't want to admit it. Instead, they prefer to maintain the myth that the brain is a machine and the brain is us; we cannot change it in any discernible way because the brain maintains its homeostasis. We may as well accept our base-level human condition, more negative than positive as it may be.

With quantum neuroscience to guide you, you now can use science to take yourself from a transactional lifestyle (What is in it for me?) to a more intelligent transformational life style where the questions you must ask yourself are:

If I am not for myself who am I?
If I am only for myself what am I?

We declare. Here is the summary of the message of this book:

Our new quantum neuroscience solves the materialists' hard problems and fully explains the human condition of separateness you are dealt with, that your brain gives you through evolutionary, genetic and environmental conditioning that the materialists emphasize. The brain is the boss when you live in this base-level human condition you are dealt with. But make no mistake: the new science unambiguously says that you are the real boss of your life, not the brain. You can prove it via creatively rewiring your brain using quantum principles. The new science also helps you to optimize the use of your brain by actualizing your potentialities. Optimize how? Optimize the functioning by training your brain to harmonize with the heart. Optimize by awakening the latent higher functions in some of brain's regions. Only then can you tap into your real intelligence.

A New Way to Think about the Brain and Live the Brain: Questions to Ponder upon

Thus, this book is about a new paradigm to think about the brain for specialists and owners alike, a new paradigm that quantum physics and experimental data impose upon us. We suggest that as you read the book, you do some thinking, and if you like an idea why not check it out and live it as well? And transform. Here is a start:

1. What is consciousness? Convince yourself that, 1) consciousness is not a special energy emanated from the brain; 2) consciousness is not an object even though some people use the intriguing phrase "quantum field" to call it; 3) Consciousness is not a hologram either.

2. Think more on what quantum field stands for. A field in physics means potential force. So, quantum field is the causal force that changes possibility into actuality. In quantum science, we see it as conscious choice and we formally call it downward causation. Do you agree?

3. The Indian spiritual tradition defines consciousness as *sat-chit-ananda*, or the existence-awareness-happiness trio. In view of quantum science, do you agree? Do you want to live by it?

4. What defines a quantum object? Textbooks say, a quantum object is both a wave and a particle. Waves spread out; particles are localized. How can the same object be both? Some people call this the paradox of wave-particle duality. Quantum science is proposing a resolution. Understand and try to apply it to your experiences of feeling and thinking.

5. What is non-locality? How does the experimentally verified idea of non-locality lead to the idea of oneness and consciousness? Think about *that* before you agree

with the book's theory. Also, have you experienced expansion of consciousness and happiness that comes with it? If not, try some of the suggestions given here.

6. What is the relationship between consciousness and the brain? Does the brain produce consciousness or does consciousness creates the brain and the world to have experience? Why is this important?

7. Consciousness collapses possibility into actuality via choice. In your ordinary experiences, you also have many instances of making a choice. Is it the same kind of choice, or different?

8. Spiritual traditions and transpersonal psychology both posit that we have two selves in agreement with quantum science. Neuroscience data is verifying the idea. What is your personal evidence for the dual nature of the self, if any?

9. We have four different objects of experience – sensory physical objects, vital feeling objects, mental meaning objects, and intuitive archetypal objects. Are you familiar with them? In isolation? In conjunction with another? Think and elaborate upon your experiences.

10. Quantum science proposes that our experiences come from potentialities of consciousness. Additionally, it also says that the subtle experiences help consciousness to make purposive operational software for our organs including the brain. This is an important turn from how traditional neuroscientists look at the brain. What is your thinking?

11. The idea of rewiring the brain is popular today. Do you think the idea makes any sense unless you are the

boss of the brain? Think about that. What would be your objectives for such rewiring?

12. The neocortex we are born with is made for producing a self-identity and for rational thinking. And yet the psychologist Carl Jung discovered that a lot of people use the brain also for intuitive thinking. This is an example of a change in neocortical function. This is the kind of thing we call optimizing the brain. Would you like to make similar changes in your brain and optimize?

13. What ideas of this chapter do you find personally empowering? Why?

CHAPTER 2

Behold! There is a Quantum Science of *All* Human Experiences

Does the brain create "I"? Does it create "me"? Materialists look at reality as if it is made of objects. Elementary particles make atoms, atoms make molecules, and molecules make bulk matter that includes neurons. If the brain is made of such bulk matter of neurons, it would be an object. Making a subject or self or I out of objects is an impossible feat.

So, these materialist brain scientists hone on to the "me". But in the way we look at it, even the "me" is not an object; it is an *objectified subject*. To be sure it is programmed to be the CPU of a whole bunch of personality programs. In this way, it is hierarchical (as in father ruling children) whereas the "I" of the quantum self is not so simply hierarchical. Yet, in the ultimate reckoning, the existence of the "me" is tied to the subject "I". The "me" is a part of the pair "I/me" albeit the "I" has gone implicit in the ego-self that we commonly experience.

Materialists talk about subjective qualia which essentially is a subjective experience that can be explicitly felt, as *the* something to be reckoned with. A lot is made of the color qualia, how the experience of the color is different for different people, displaying maximum subjectivity. If we can solve this problem, we arrive at the promised land, a viable materialist theory of the brain and consciousness, we are told. It is a "hard" problem, materialists think, but not impossible. In our opinion, this is wrong thinking. As soon as you have uttered the concept of "experience", the problem of subject/self as an experiencer is back, because an experience has to have two poles: the experiencer/subject (implicit if not explicit) and experienced/object. And moreover, you may have opened a new can of worms by using the word "felt" which people normally reserve for the past tense of the word "feel". Feelings are an anathema to material monism because they are not computable.

Additionally, people who have the pure "I"-experiences, and there are quite a few of these people, tell us that these experiences are striking, full of happiness, spiritual joy. In the olden days, people used to classify these experiences as *numina* as opposed to phenomena, the word that they used for ordinary experiences that include the ego-experience of "me". It almost seems like the materialists are ignoring the essence of human experiences when they choose the mere color qualia as an explanation. What is the qualia of a noumenon? It is the expanded consciousness, the touch of Oneness! It is another anathema to materialist thinking.

Behold! Ye of materialist ilk. The problem you have in comprehending the situation of consciousness is a spiritual one. Because of your constricted consciousness, you seldom experience *numina*, perhaps never. Hence, scientists of your kind, by denying spirituality, deny yourselves and your followers the understanding of what consciousness is really about – expansion, the experience of which brings us joy or *ananda*.

Take the case of the great Sigmund Freud, for example. Freud had numinous experiences a few times; he called them oceanic feelings; altogether an appropriate description of expanded consciousness. A noumenon does expand your sense of who you are. "I am this whole world," said Erwin Schrodinger, a co-discoverer of quantum physics, who was no stranger to these experiences and was not a materialist at heart. But Freud, being a materialist, pooh-poohed the experience calling it "infantile helplessness".

Still progress, albeit at snail speed, is taking place in the scientists' thinking even though the mainstream still vows for material monism. Today, many scientists openly admit that they have creative numinous experiences of "flow," in which your ego (me) and your quantum self (I) play together so seamlessly that you feel the joy of flow the whole time. And this thawing of the scientific mindset includes neuroscientists.

Even a couple of decades ago, a philosopher named Daniel Dennett went around in conferences declaring that he is a zombie (not the TV favorite night creatures but robots, fully mechanical) just to make the point he had proposed in his book *Consciousness Explained*. But in his more recent book on neuroscience, *The New Science of Consciousness*, the neuroscientist Paul Nunez qualifies Dennett's claim that we are robots. "We are zombies or robots with experience," he says. According to him, we are philosophical zombies or philosophical robots, p-zombies or p-robots for short—zombies or robots with c-factor (I guess the 'c' stands for consciousness) experience.

Can one be a zombie and have experience? Is that possible? You wonder. Nunez thinks it is possible if experiences are harmless epiphenomena, secondary ornamental phenomena of the brain, with no causal tooth, causal ability or efficacy.

Are humans organic but mechanical robots with experiences, p-robots? The debate comes down to causal power. We seem to have free will even at the "me" level of experience. We can *choose* our experiences to a limited extent.

I am reminded of a cartoon in the comic strip *Pearls before Swine*. The character called Rat is complaining to another, Goat, "I buy things, thing, things, and I am not happy. So, I buy bigger things, better things, faster things. But I am still not happy." In the next frame, the character called Pig appears and as he flies away with the help of helium balloons he shouts, "Maybe life is about experience." In the next frame Rat is cranky. "I hate it when he does that," he says. Don't be surprised if a neuroscientist becomes cranky when you mention quantum science or consciousness!

There is brain data (see chapter 7) to support that we have a modicum of free will even at the level of ego to choose our experience. And at the quantum level, we have all the obvious causal power of creativity. The staunch materialist goes on denying the causal power of our experience of free will, or even of creativity.

The God or Oneness hypothesis of traditions, even when properly understood as a Oneness, by itself does not give us much clue about how to live in the world because it has no theory of how consciousness is manifest in the brain, how our separateness arises. The primacy of matter hypothesis can explain our "me" (sans free will) but does not explain how the brain acquires a creative "I". Neither paradigm can explain how the "I" with new ideas but no memories to give them form, and the "me" with no new ideas but plenty of memory to give the new ideas the much-needed form, together leads to a creative product that includes our own transformation.

The primacy of matter hypothesis in biology – supposedly a science of life – cannot distinguish non-living and living. It just incorporates the distinguishing properties of the living – its ability to distinguish between itself and its environment, its ability to evolve, its ability to form communities, etc. – in the definition of the living. How is this different from Eastern religions asserting that despite our separateness from each other we are all God, all interconnected by a Oneness? These religions and even other religions at least tell us about empirical practices for improving the human condition. The best materialist science can do is to tell us how to cope with the human condition.

Today we suffer from a polarization between two worldviews, one based on religion, the other based on materialist science. It has become a cultural war. Both religions and materialist science are stuck at the same knot: the relationship of the unity and the separateness; the relationship between consciousness and brain.

As stated before, I (Amit) have solved this problem decades ago. In this book, we will explore the solution further in view of the latest data of neuroscience and our own latest clearer thinking on the subject.

Only You the Reader Who Wants to Awaken Can Stop Newton's Sleep

The eighteenth-century romantic poet William Blake wrote these very memorable lines complaining about Newtonian deterministic physics and the then aborning philosophy of material monism:

May God us keep

From Single vision and Newton's sleep.

Neuroscientists of the materialist kind behave like sleepwalkers, with a very narrow tunnel vision. The fact is that quantum physics has overthrown Newtonian physics. The fact is material objects are waves of possibility; in the least, it takes a conversion of these possibilities into actual events in space and time through a quantum measurement in which an observer is a must. These findings are not debatable.

So why do these neuroscientists write research papers and books claiming that the brain does this and the brain does that? The brain remains a possibility until the conversion act of collapse takes place, and when that happens, the brain seems to have acquired a self, an observership.

Neuroscientists of the younger generation assure us that things are changing. However, one has to be pragmatic enough to realize that a paradigm shift of such momentous importance takes time; lots and lots of vested interest are involved. In the meantime, though, do you, the reader need to be a sleepwalker? Resort to your common sense when reading a book about the brain that spreads ignorance and myths. Why do you read a brain book? Because you expect such books to tell you something about how to live better, how to make your human condition happier and more effective in the world. Can a bagful of molecules governed by deterministic laws (that's what the brain is according to materialist scientists) help you to get you out of your limitations?

The entire scientific culture is in denial. American English has a new word, "woke." You are woke when you don't deny the truth of the situation anymore.

Boost your common sense with some basic quantum physics that we shall present in the next few sections of this chapter. And most of all, remember there is no need to play the blame game; the materialist neuroscience despite its limitations is serving a huge purpose that is completely in synch with the movement of consciousness. It is giving us valuable data. Let's learn together how to evaluate this data from the primacy of consciousness point of view.

Most of all remember! Only you can take humanity to embrace the new quantum worldview by applying and proving quantum science's usefulness in your life.

Besides the "me"-experience, another human experience that the materialists do not deny is thought. Most brain scientists look at the brain as a computer with mental software of its own making. Can the brain do that?

We think with our mental software and the brain certainly has an association with that software. This much is undebatable. Thought has meaning and you know you can use your computer to make a software of your own mental meaning. See the problem? As far as you know, silicon computers cannot process meaning and make software by themselves, only you can use it to make and run your meaning software.

There is now quite a convincing proof that computers cannot process meaning given by the philosopher John Searle. In the eighties when I (Amit) first read Searle's proof, I immediately concluded that the brain, since it is a computer of sorts, cannot process meaning. Meaning-giving mind must be non-physical. But to my surprise, Searle later wrote a book, *The Rediscovery of the Mind*, in which he concluded differently that brain's ability goes beyond that of a mere computer, the brain somehow can cognize.

Beliefs can do that to you. A psych student is studying the cognitive effect of cutting off a frog's leg on its hearing ability; he cuts off one leg, and says, "Frog, jump." The frog jumps. No discernible effect, the student writes in his note book.

The student takes a second leg off and repeats, "Frog, jump." The frog complies. The student makes the same note. The student takes off another leg and repeats. No change. The frog still jumps.

Now the student takes the fourth and final leg off and gives his order, "Frog, jump." This time the frog does not jump. The student writes in his notebook: Only after all four legs are cut off does the frog loses its hearing ability. He forgot that there is a simpler explanation.

The brain cannot cognize. There is a straightforward simple answer: it is consciousness that cognizes with the help of a nonphysical organizing principle called the mind. The neuroscientist Alva Noë has reached that conclusion with convincing argument even without using quantum science. Read his book, *Out of Our Heads: Why You are Not Your Brain and Other Lessons from the Biology of Consciousness.*

Some brain-scientists toy with the idea that there is a unique objective meaning of everything to convince us that the brain can assign meaning. But of course, our experience says otherwise: meaning is subjective. When we understand other-people's meaning, more often than not it has a unique flavor. Everyone understands in his or her own way, right? There is also the compelling question of new meaning. Our creativity is about new meaning.

Is mind non-physical then? If so, how does it interact with the brain which is physical? They have nothing in common; they need a mediator, but where is the mediator? So, neuroscientists in the main avoid this dualism of mind and brain and think mind is a creation of the brain.

But then too, the thorny question of, "Can the brain process meaning?" still remains. It certainly can process what is programmed into it – old meaning. Then the question is how the old meaning got there? Perhaps, from other people? True, but how did it get into the first person who thought it? And of course, we ourselves have new thoughts that have new meaning, as for example, creative thought. Many brain scientists deny creativity to fit the brain to their materialist thinking. Do you see yourself as incapable of creativity?

It is the opposite; you would like to know how to enhance your creativity, how to optimize your mental function of creativity. And undeniably, it is a question for the brain as well.

I think, and I call the thinking part of me my mind. Mind is not the brain. Consciousness uses the intermediary of the mind for programming meaning processing ability in our brains. In other words, the neuronal memory of thoughts acts as the trigger for activating the mental software to the brain-hardware. The activation of the trigger automatically plays out the correlated mental memory/software causing the confusion (fig. 2).

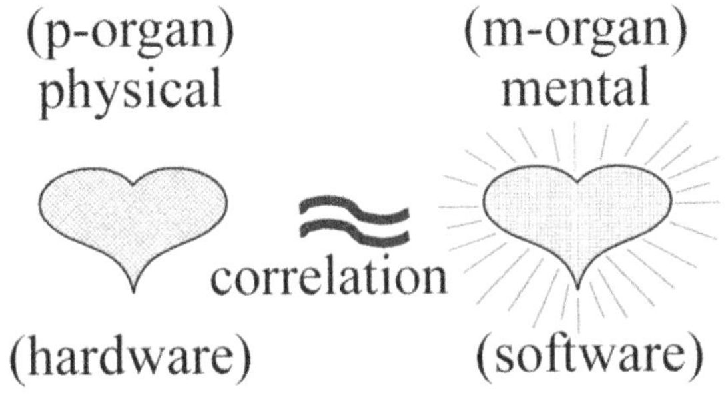

Figure 2. Correlated physical and mental memory

There is no doubt about it. Memory is brain-mind memory; mind and brain work together to make memory.

Mind enables consciousness to make sense of all the material stimuli the brain processes. When? In the process of perception itself (details in next chapter). Why? So that it can create ordered structures out of the chaotic images of the physical world that the brain makes.

Perception plus meaning-giving thought is cognition. But thought is not the only means of cognition in the brain; there is also feeling by which mammals cognize. This ability is largely suppressed in us. Understanding the brain should help us reclaim this capacity.

Does thought only result from existing brain-mind memory? According to material monism, it does. On the other hand, the new science explored in this book says no. We have creativity, ability of intuitive and creative thinking that breaks away from the past memory. Crucial here is the recent finding of neuroplasticity. Brain has the capacity of making new neuronal connections, new representations of our creative thoughts. This new brain-mind memory paves the way we change, transform.

Neuroplasticity of the brain is the enabler of change and creativity. Although materialists de-emphasize its importance, neuroplasticity is a breakthrough discovery in the new science of the brain because it validates the idea of changing the brain with inner creativity. In 2004, the movie *What the Bleep Do We Know?* was released, in which I (Amit) played a small role in my capacity of a quantum physicist. You may have seen it; it is about a struggle of a young woman with her alcohol addiction. The movie ends with hope based on two promising ideas: 1) quantum inner creativity and 2) brain's neuroplasticity. In this book, we will demonstrate that this hope has now found fruition. You can change, even the habit of addiction, even addiction to material monism or any other form of fundamentalism.

Let's talk about those negative emotions that create helter-skelter in us and our interactions with the world. The religious worldview puts negative emotions such as anger, violence, competitiveness, domination, fear, lust, jealousy, envy, etc. in the domain of the evil as opposed to good. Brain scientists have done better; they have identified places in the brain's interior middle (also called limbic brain) – the negative emotional brain circuits – as the source of our negative emotions. Negative emotions create mental stress and eventually might lead to the chronic diseases that we all dread such as cancer, heart disease and autoimmune diseases like arthritis.

Only a little contemplation will convince you that your emotions are a combination of thoughts and feelings. Of course, biologists, and that include neuroscientists, have no room for feeling in their worldview, no theory for it. For them, an emotion is a brain response to suitable stimulus; as such, the unconscious emotional responses of the midbrain are a byproduct of Darwinian evolution; they may satisfy some survival necessity, but that is all. However, in the absence of any viable distinction between unconscious and conscious memory-making, such models are simplistic and of dubious validity.

The truth is neuroscientists don't know what feelings are, and how the brain's negative emotional brain circuits came about and how they work; so they cannot help us very much in abating them or balancing them, or transcending them, can they? They can talk about emotional intelligence all they like (there are many books), but it is just talk; it does not help us transform our emotional response.

A suitable stimulus (a cobra ready to strike) is seen by our primitive eyes and relayed by the brain area called thalamus directly to the amygdala where it elicits the instinctual memory of emotions (theorized dubiously as unconscious memory) which calls for fast motor action – the flight or fight response. The pathway bypasses the neocortex (fig. 3). Only later, the visual cortex, its eyes and apparatuses of consciousness come into play and thus we experience a negative emotion. This the best the neuroscience can do. Read J. Ledoux' book, *The Emotional Brain*.

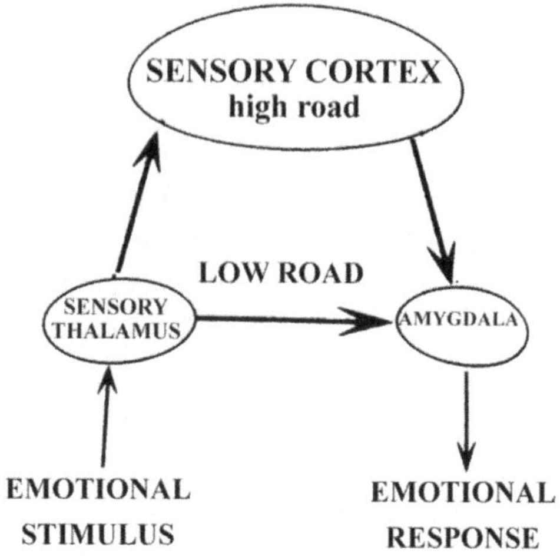

Figure. 3 The flight-fight response. The pathway through amygdala bypassing the neocortex.

The essential problem with negative emotions according to this picture is this. Whereas the brain memory we make consciously is the software we can control, the memory in the amygdala cannot be controlled by us. The distinction is this. The memory we do control is easy to overwrite, but the memory we don't control is not. Thus, in conclusion, the conventional wisdom that says you cannot control or get rid of your instinctual negative emotions is true; and these negative emotions are virtually part of your nature.

The new science is able to explain not only how instinctual software is made but also what evolutionary mechanism produces such software that seemingly becomes autonomous, out of our control. Understanding this, we are also able to theorize how to gain back such control.

Pleasure and Addiction

There are also pleasure centers in the brain. When we eat or have sex, these pleasure centers of the brain are activated with the production of brain molecules of dopamine, endorphin and other such molecules of pleasure. These neuro-molecules, like opiates, fit into brain receptors as keys fit into their lock's keyholes, giving us explosive pleasure or even euphoria. These molecules of emotion make pleasure so attractive, so important in our lives! Read Candace Pert's delightful book, *Molecules of Emotion*, if you want to get a grasp of how compelling these molecules are. No wonder, people get lost in what they have to offer.

In summary, there are two brain aspects of pleasure to remember:

- The dopamine level in your brain indicates pleasure; a steady high level of dopamine. If the dopamine level starts falling, that's the signal of displeasure.
- The onset of pleasure is indicated by a burst of neuro chemicals like opioids and endorphins which we have already mentioned, as well as norepinephrine and the hormone oxytocin.

The problem is that pleasure follows the Sufi dictum of "this too shall pass." Actually, it is way worse. Evolution and survival necessity have produced a tendency in the brain to look out for sources of pain much more than for sources of pleasure. Here are some tips about the brain that brain scientists warn us about:

- **Anxiety:** When we vegetate, the brain goes into a default mode called self-agency. Unfortunately, this default mode of the brain has a built-in tendency via evolution and development to look out for dangers, track the environment for possible threats to your safety. We experience this vigilance as anxiety.
- **More sensitivity toward negative emotional stimuli than to positive**: Researchers showed subjects happy or neutral faces side by side with violent faces, both consciously and subliminally. Guess what? Even subliminally the brain is able to process the violent face much more rapidly via the thalamus and amygdala of course bypassing the neocortex. Such is the power of negative emotional brain circuits.
- **Negative gets preference for storage**: Researchers have concluded that "your brain is Velcro for negative experiences and Teflon for positive ones." Apparently, the brain compartment of the hippocampus sees to this.
- **The brain gives more weight to the negative compared to the positive**: Even successful people feel helpless when failure hits them, even if they have experienced multiple failures before. Accident victims suffer more than lottery winners enjoy their

success. Have a fight with your spouse and verify it directly. It will take you on the average five events of positivity to overcome the effect of that one event of negativity.

- **You cannot unlearn the negative**: There is evidence that even if you get reconditioned against a particular negative to deal with it, there will be a residue which will be triggered when the going gets tough.

Okay, we've spoken enough about negativity. The good news is that although making positive emotional brain circuits with quantum creativity may not compellingly work, they work partially at least to help us balance our negativity to a manageable extent. Furthermore, there is one way to avoid negativity that always works: to live increasingly in the quantum self. How do we make positive emotional brain circuits? How do we optimize the brain to operate more in the quantum-self modality? We do both by using the quantum aspects of the movements of thought and feelings.

Thus, the important question, how do we know that thoughts and feelings are quantum in their behavior? Let's delve into this question in the next section.

First, both physical and psyche worlds remain as possibilities until consciousness gives them substantiality by manifesting an actual experience.

Second, there are differences between physical and psyche substances as we experience them. One big difference is the externality of the macro world of our shared perception of the physical domain. In contrast, experiences of the psyche are internal.

At the micro level, physical objects are quantum; but as they make big conglomerates acquiring bigger and bigger masses, the quantum movement gives way to deterministic Newtonian movement. The wave of potentiality of the center of mass of macro objects made of matter still spreads when left alone, but they spread sluggishly to the extreme. So sluggishly that when you and I look at a chair, there is such little range of potentialities of position of the center of mass to choose from, that you and I end up choosing virtually the same position. The leeway of choice we have in this case can be calculated to be of the order of 10^{-17} cm, too tiny to discern except for laser assisted measurements. Naturally, we think we are looking at the same chair at the same position; we reach a consensus that the chair is outside of us. This consensus agreement about our experience is what we call objectivity. In this way, all objectivity is weak objectivity; quantum physics does not allow any other kind of objectivity.

There is one other very important thing about this weakly objective material world of our consensus perception. It not only seems out there, but it also gives the appearance that it is always out there independent of whether anyone is looking at it or not. In the sixties, an avant-garde physicist made quite a commotion with his paper in the magazine *Physics Today* called *Is the Moon There When Nobody is Looking at It?* No, it isn't, says quantum physics. The moon manifests only in somebody's experience, and only momentarily. It appears in manifestation from potentiality; after manifestation and experience, it goes back to potentiality. The fact that the moon, a large macroscopic object is always more or less exactly where we expect to find it gives us the illusion that it must always be out there manifest.

In comparison to the physical, the world of our psyche is always experienced as internal, subtle, impermanent, and private, not shared. This internality is the definitive evidence that the objects of the psyche – thoughts, feelings, intuitions – are quantum.

Let's talk about thought. As Descartes correctly intuited, mental substance is indivisible, we cannot reduce it to smaller and smaller pieces, nor is there is any micro thought out of which the macro thought is made. So, the mental world is considered a whole, one that physicists sometimes call an infinite medium. There can be waves in such infinite media, modes of movement that are quantum possibility waves. We directly observe and actualize these quantum modes without using any amplifying macro mental measurement apparatus (there isn't any; the physical brain provides the measurement apparatus for mental objects). But we pay a price. In between actualizations and experiences, the mental modes become waves of possibility and are subject to rapid quantum movement; they quickly become large pools of possible meanings. What this means is that between my collapse and your collapse, between my thinking and your thinking about the same stimulus, the quantum mental modes would have expanded in possibility so much that it becomes unlikely that you will be able to collapse exactly the same thought as me. Therefore, two different people, subject to the same stimuli cannot ordinarily have the same thoughts; thoughts are private, they are experienced internally.

This internality is the positive proof that thoughts or mental meanings are quantum, and more. By the same token of internality, we can safely assume that the vital world of feeling and the supramental world of intuition are also quantum worlds.

Additional compelling evidence of the quantum nature of these subtle experiences comes from experimental data about occasional non-locality and discontinuity of these experiences.

The Psyche and the Physical are Parallel Aspects of One Consciousness

The quantum paradigm enables us to construct a science of all our experiences -- sensing, feeling, thinking, and intuiting, because all we need to realize is that they all are quantum potentialities within consciousness to choose from. This is not dualism simply because consciousness mediates the interaction of these parallel worlds of potentiality within consciousness, and does it non-locally, without any signals.

You can think of all these four worlds of potentiality within consciousness in another useful way: quantum psychophysical parallelism. All these quantum worlds, three of them defining the psyche that we experience internally, and the fourth, the "external" material world go on in parallel and consciousness maintains their parallelism via conscious intention.

So, there you are! The brain is wonderful: it represents consciousness to give us a sense of self. It represents the mind as software programs giving us an effortless entry to the world of meaning. It even gives us brain circuits of instinctual negative emotions producing quick seemingly unconscious actions that can save our life.

However, the brain gives us good experiences and also takes them away. We suffer a lot from those negative emotional brain circuits. The brain does not distinguish between imagination and actuality. So, if consciousness uses our mind to imagine that my boss is a tiger, the brain will trigger the instinctual fear circuit and elicit the same flight-fight response as if my boss was a real tiger creating unnecessary emotional stress harmful to health.

The inability to distinguish between imagination and actuality, between what is experienced here and now and what is experienced from elicitation of memory of the past makes brain a simulator of "virtual reality." When people ask you, "Have you ever thought of any use of all the work artificial intelligence researchers are doing on virtual reality?" your learned response should be, "We already live in a virtual reality created by our brain!" Neuroscientists have verified that only a small fraction of what we experience comes from what the eye sees and what the outside input on the occipital lobe of the brain is. Brain creates our world from memory of the past and projections into the future; and thus "we live before and after and pine for what is not."

The brain is built to give more weight to the negative than the positive: "Our sweetest songs are those that tell of saddest thought". Moreover, we cannot even fully erase the negative emotions from the brain.

And finally, the pleasure from the neurochemicals can be addictive. So, at this stage of our evolution our human condition is far from optimal.

Let's lay out the base-level human condition with which we are designed by the laws of the universe and our evolution once more:

1. We have a quantum self/ego, I/me polarity in the way we experience our subject-hood. Right now, worldview, culture etc. are all pulling us more toward the 'me'-pole. So, we have become transactional, our consciousness is constricted and much worse off. The "me" that each of us develop, is a borrowed one, borrowed from others via processing other people's meaning as information. Thus, our individuality or heterogeneity is no more than a statistical homogeneity – statistically determined and predictable.

2. There is currently an epidemic of information-processing at the expense of meaning-processing. The greed of the information industry has created real obstacles against studying the debilitating effect of information processing on the brain. Even so, there is now a consensus that the effect is a dumbing-down of the brain. This adds to the "me"-centeredness and rampant narcissism that we see in some of today's youth and adult.

3. We have negative emotional brain circuits built into the brain; part of these circuits seems to be instinctual

and its unconscious triggering is followed by immediate survival related action and later thoughts of emotion. Unfortunately, imagination enters the picture, a habit we call mentalization of feeling, and we misuse our negative emotional brain circuits and cause ourselves much mental/emotional stress.

4. And finally, we have pleasure circuits giving us dopamine, endorphin, and other molecular "high" when activated. This can lead to addiction. There are opiate drugs that work on the brain like endorphin does. One habit leads to another and drug and drug-like addictions are hard to quit.

5. In the final reckoning, yes, "this too shall pass" is true of all emotions – negative and positive. But the negative takes much longer to pass.

Mind you! Since this is our natural design, this is perfectly normal. If we engage these tendencies with moderation, we can live a satisfactory life as far as it goes, perhaps with a lot of ups and downs. The negative emotions are mostly downers; so, we tend to balance them with "me"-centered pursuits of pleasure. And this can cause problems, addiction for example. It is perfectly normal, if you are a woman, to cope with your emotional ennui by buying a pair of high-heels that gives you a feeling of sexual attractiveness and lifts your spirit. Or, if you are a man, playing a computer game. But when this becomes an addiction, and you become a shopaholic or an information addict, it is pathological.

Positive Emotions

Where do feelings originate? The brain? Not a good answer obviously, because animals without the brain also have feelings, even plants. Don't be persuaded otherwise; there is much evidence that plants and animals can feel. If you have a relationship with household plants, you won't need convincing. In the current information age, loneliness has become an epidemic; people have become so individualistic and self-absorbed, they have only digital friends that do not satisfy. So, they are buying household plants as a cure for loneliness; pets too. The advantage of household plants is that they don't need much care.

For single cells and plants, feelings originate in connection of the cell itself. Even single cells need functional (non-physical) blueprints of vital software we introduced before – the liturgical/morphogenetic fields. For higher animals and humans, feelings originate in the body in connection with the body organs and their associated functional software of more complex liturgical/morphogenetic fields.

There are 7 major centers in the body located roughly along the spine; they are called chakras (fig. 4). Notice that the chakra points are all close to one or more important body organs. Notice also the highest three of the chakras are located in the brain – one (the fifth) at the speech center, one (the sixth) at the prefrontal cortex, the last one (the seventh) at the parietal lobe.

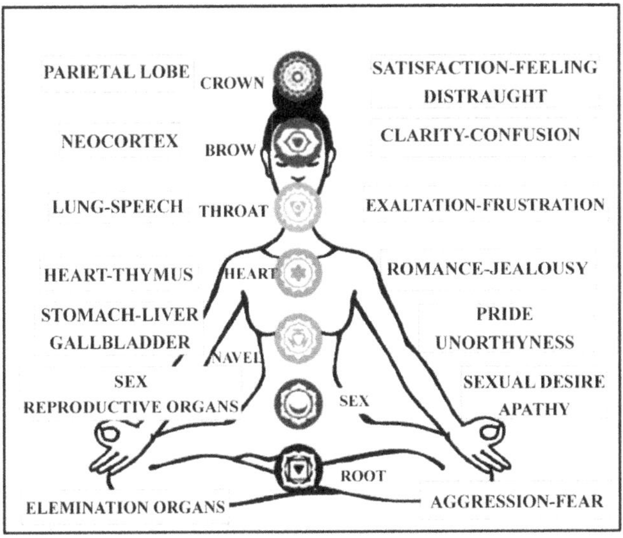

Figure 4. The 7 Main Chakras according to tradition

A big accomplishment of the quantum worldview is a scientific explanation of the biology of feelings and the chakras. The essence of the theory is that a physical organ always works in conjunction with its liturgical counterpart, its universal software – a vital organ, V organ. And this vital organ or vital software, just like the mind, is quantum in its origin, the liturgical fields. This makes a living cell and a living organ behave in the quantum way, opening them to new potentialities of huge new behavior beyond the explanatory power of the Newtonian conceptualization. Henceforth, whenever we mention a living cell or an organ including a neuron or a brain component, it will stand for the physical organ-vital software duo (fig. 5). The macroscopically distinguishable states of possibility that consciousness chooses from when actualizing such a duo are the states of old potentiality of the universal vital software plus new potentialities for a creative response. The physical organ acts as a measurement apparatus.

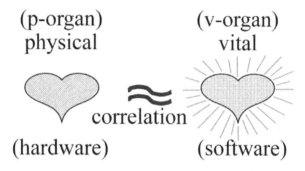

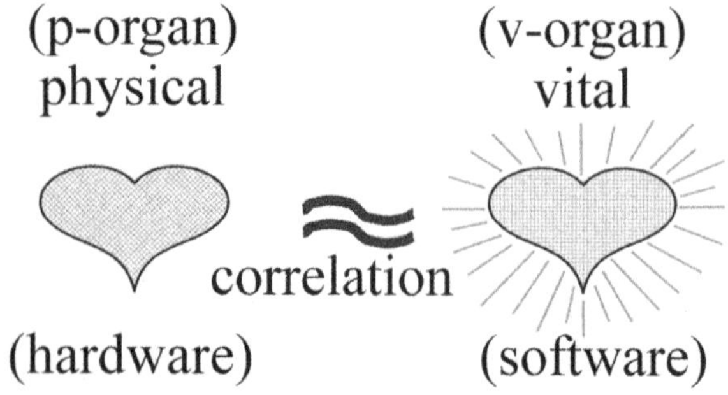

Figure 5. The P-organ V-organ correlated duo

For reasons of survival, during our evolution, the brain has taken over the control over instinctual feelings connected with the lowest three chakras related to maintenance of the body and sexual reproduction. The heart chakra is mostly associated with love but that is a higher function. The normal function of the heart chakra is defensiveness connected with the immune system, and the brain seems to have control over that too via the mind.

Now, let's get back to the chakras. Here is a chakra-by-chakra description of the vital function, the corresponding physical organs that represent the vital blueprints of the function, and the associated feelings:

Root chakra: The vital function is waste elimination. The organs that express the vital blueprints of the function are the kidneys, the bladder, and the large intestine (rectum and anus). The associated feelings are aggression, competitiveness, and fear.

Note: People of chronic constipation have risk aversion; they live in fear.

Sex chakra: The biological ~~vital~~ function is reproduction, its blueprints represented by the reproductive organs – uterus, ovaries, prostate, testes, etc. The associated feelings are sexual desire and unfulfilled lust or apathy.

Navel chakra: The vital function is maintenance and the organ representations are the stomach, small intestine, liver, gall bladder, and the pancreas. The associated feelings are pride, narcissism, and unworthiness.

Special note: When you are unsure of yourself, you might feel butterflies in your stomach. Rings a bell?

Heart chakra: The normal vital function is defensiveness (when the distinction between me and the other is operative) and vulnerability (when the defensiveness tends to relax). The organ representation is the thymus gland and the immune system. The thymus gland is a crucial component of the immune system whose job is to distinguish between what molecules belongs to one's own body (me) and what does not (not me) and get rid of intruders.

We feel romance when the immune system function of me / not-me distinction is suspended; this is when the vital energy of this chakra is additionally boosted and positively. If the love energy is depleted however, the feeling is jealousy, loss, grief, and hurt.

Why is the name given to this specific chakra "heart" chakra? When the immune system's function is suspended, the heart shines forth. So, the name is quite appropriate. Yet, it is also misleading. Because, we are talking about a higher function of the heart when we talk about love; if we suspend our defense, then only love, this higher function shines forth.

Special note: Now this one should ring a bell in everyone; who doesn't remember being a teenager and experiencing romance as heartthrobs? When we are older, the romantic feelings abate a little and are experienced as tingles or just warmth. The explanation is simply that your immune system has accepted the intrusion of your romantic partner into the vital field; in other words, as part of "you." When that expansion of who you are happens, it is possible for you to give anything to your partner, even your life. This is one of the reasons why we enjoy the movie character James Bond, who might be a romantic lover for a particular partner for only about six weeks, but he takes undue risks to save his partner's life.

Bonus special note: The description above of romantic love sounds pretty unconditional, doesn't it? Is it? Unfortunately, no. Remember the brain takes over; the brain makes romantic love quite conditional. No wonder the comedian Jerry Seinfeld joked, "The brain is a sneaky organ." Neuroscientists have studied the specific parts of the brain organs activated in the early stages of romantic love when it is the most intense. The activated areas are (Surprise! Surprise!) the ventral tegmental area (VTA) – a major organ of the reward system – along with the caudet nucleus which is also associated with reward. These researchers showed lovers pictures of their romantic partner and also a neutral picture of somebody the lovers don't specially care about. As soon as lovers see the picture of their romantic lover, their VTA and caudet nucleus light up. No such reaction with neutral pictures. Undoubtedly, romantic lovers are looking for reward in the form of intense pleasure now that the brain is in the game.

Perhaps two other kinds of love: maternal love and love in the form of altruism is also instinctualized via the brain. Mirror neurons, neurons that enable us to mirror and experience what another person in our immediate environment is experiencing, also enable us to feel sympathy as well as a sympathetic response that we call altruism.

Do mirror neurons enable the ability some psychologists call "theory of [other people's] mind?" The idea is that some of us can manipulate other people better because we have this uncanny ability of knowing what the other person is thinking. We think that these people just have a better understanding of neuro-linguistic programming, the body language that we all unconsciously exhibit. Empathy on the other hand is a quantum response; it requires non-locality!

Throat chakra: The biological vital function is self-expression and the organs that represent it are the lungs, throat, speech organs, the organs for hearing, and also the thyroid gland. The associated feelings are the exultation of expression, and the opposite, frustration for the inability to express.

Note: Our throat dries up when we are unable to express ourselves.

Brow chakra: The usual vital function is mentation in the form of rational thinking, gaining conceptual knowledge. The organ is neo-cortex in the form of the prefrontal cortex, right behind our forehead, where the mind is mapped. The associated feelings are clarity and confusion.

Something interesting: You will notice if you pay attention, that today there is a general ennui, a general lack of vitality in this chakra. Mass hypnosis of replacing meaning-processing by information-processing is the culprit.

Crown chakra: The biological vital function is to produce a body image. The organ is the parietal lobe (the posterior superior parietal lobe, to be exact). This body image is sometimes called the homunculus (fig. 6).

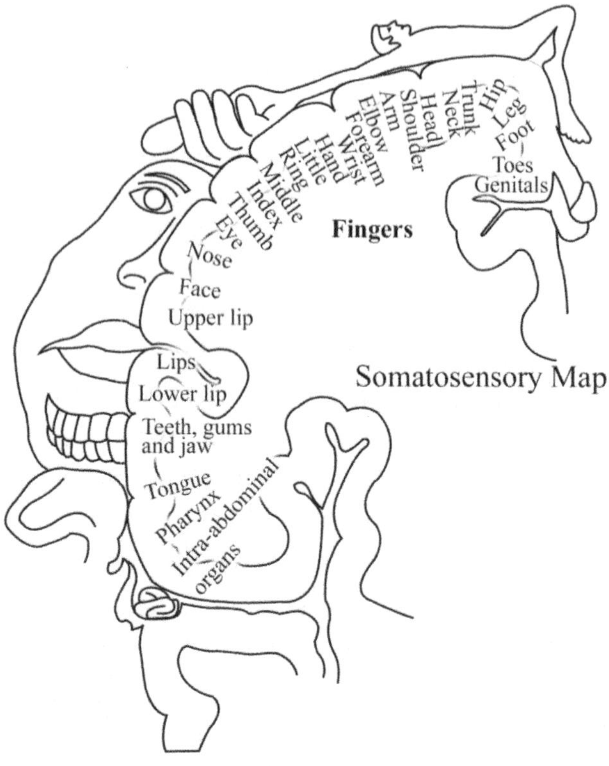

Figure 6. The body image created by the parietal lobe. It is called the homunculus

The associated feelings are satisfaction (with our body image), a sense and feeling of well-being and their opposite, feeling distraught (dissatisfaction with the body image). Anorexic teenage girls have a major problem with their body image; they are never satisfied with it. They develop a major blockage of the vital energies at the crown chakra.

Here's something interesting. Notice that in the homunculus, the foot and toe areas are close to the sex areas. This is likely the reason for foot fetish that some people have. And indeed, some women experience orgasmic delight with foot rubs and toe-sucking.

All the chakras, when they fully open and acquire new functional software, are connected with our positive noble feelings such as courage connected with the root and navel chakra, libido or life-force connected with the sex chakra, self-worth and self-love in the navel, unconditional love at the heart chakra, joy of creative learning and expression at the throat chakra, curiosity and satisfaction that following up intuition with creative insight brings us at the brow chakra, suspension of physical attachment to one's body at the crown chakra that gives us out-of-the-body experiences of flying, and for these noble feelings there are no instinctual brain circuits. Not yet.

Unlike their negative counterpart, there are few built-in brain circuits connected with the positive noble feelings in our normal human condition. Here is the game changer to consider: religions think that compassion for others comes to us naturally. The quantum worldview corrects this mistake: compassion is universally available for us, but only as potentiality. As we explore, experience, and live the positive noble emotions (feelings at these high chakras and the meaning our minds give to them) such as compassion, we make memories of them. These we call positive emotional brain circuits. Making those is a crucial part of our transformation.

The drive toward "me"-centeredness is connected with the survival instinct that is very strong in us obviously. However, we do have the occasional pure "I"-experience and so there is a drive towards that as well. This drive toward positivity and positive emotions starts with intuitions as mentioned before. We have to be sensitive toward intuitions. But the human condition is against that. This is why only a few of us can respond to this drive. Out of these few, most respond when the suffering in their life (constriction of consciousness, mental stress due to negative emotions, addiction to pleasure, etc.) reaches a point of crisis. Only a few respond to the intuitions and the archetypes because they have a healthy curiosity toward exploring human potentialities.

The important point we address in this book is our amazing brain's plasticity that allows this drive toward unity to be fulfilled if only we use its facilities skillfully. You will see. You will learn.

The obvious recipe, antidote really, to the human condition of (normal) separateness, is to develop sensitivity towards our drive towards unity that we do have, and that means primarily listening to our intuitions. Don't worry; your increased sensitivity to unity consciousness will also produce increased sensitivity to intuitions.

There are nine major archetypes: truth, love, beauty, justice, abundance, power, goodness, wholeness, and self. Of these, Truth, since it includes very finely tuned physical laws, is absolute, unchangeable. The other archetypes are quantum multifaceted objects, but all their facets have value.

We think and our brain has the capacity of making direct representations of the meaning that we think, 'brain-mind memory'. But the brain, our most advanced organ, does not have the capacity to make direct representation of the archetypes that we intuit. So, we first make representations of the intuitive experience of the archetype with thinking and/or feeling, and simultaneously follow up with representing them in our brain and body respectively via living our archetypal experiences.

That the brain helps make memory of mental meaning has been known for some time. But the fact that the body helps make memory of feelings in neurons both at the heart and at the navel chakra is a recent far-reaching breakthrough discovery. Together these representations give us the positive emotional brain circuits—our positive emotional personal software.

Here is the bad news though. Intuitions are very fleeting experiences and we cannot really make usable representations of them neither with thinking nor with feeling. Yet throughout history, we have evidence of people of transformation; we call them geniuses, spiritual masters. How did they do it? Until recently, this was a mystery that was solved by the quantum science that includes a theory of creativity. Whereas intuitions are a doorway to the archetypes, the creative "aha" insight and the subsequent mini-insights are a full-pledged intimate look at the archetypes giving us plenty of time to make vital and mental representations of them.

There is a whole process, the creative process, that takes us to the "aha" insight. On the whole, the creative process consists of: alternative preparation doing mostly) and unconscious processing (being, relaxing mostly), sudden insight, manifestation. Or abbreviated: do-be-do-be-do, insight, manifestation.

Unfortunately, creativity that people ordinarily engage with is to solve situational problems, outer or inner. This kind we call situational creativity. The creativity for discovering a new face of an archetype in suchness requires much more inner motivation. This kind of creativity we call fundamental creativity.

And this is the good news. The new theory of quantum creativity gives away the secret of creativity, the creative process. Anybody can have creative insights using the creative process, for both situational and fundamental explorations. And anybody can use brain's plasticity in the neocortex for the manifestation or embodiment of the discovered insights. In this way anybody can develop positive noble emotional brain circuits. The details of the creative process are beyond the scope of this book. The curious reader should read 1) Amit's book *Quantum Creativity* and 2) our brain sequel *The Awakening of Intelligence*.

You know it is funny that brain researchers and even many post-materialist thinkers cite the case of London taxi drivers' brain (before GPS) as an example of brain's plasticity.

Let's discuss the famous case of London cab drivers who were studied around the year 2000. These cabbies had to memorize a huge amount of data in their brain; they were required to know every street in a six miles radius area in central London before they got their taxi-driving license. And this was before GPS; so, they used their own memorized data, as well, thus reinforcing the memory. When their brains were examined, indeed, their brains' posterior hippocampi were significantly larger in size than those of control subjects who did not drive taxies. And guess what functions the posterior hippocampus performs? This part of the hippocampus has a role in spatial navigation and it also stores spatial information of the environment.

Yes! These taxi drivers had more weight, more neurons and synaptic connections in their hippocampal area because they had to learn the traffic map of London so well. Obviously, neurons multiplied in that area, suggesting plasticity.

But you know, that's not the kind of use of brain plasticity that you want. A teacher asked young Einstein, "What is the speed of sound?" Einstein said, "I do not clutter my brain with such trivia that I can look up." This is the attitude of the creative. The creative uses neuronal plasticity to create new representations of mental meaning and vital feelings that we generate from archetypal creative explorations.

So, how do you enrich your brain in creative ways? The neuroscientist Wendy Suzuki wrote the delightful book *Healthy Brain, Happy Life*, in which she suggested several ways. Dance new steps, it will enrich your motor cortex. Try a new cuisine if you want to improve your taste cortex. Watch a TED talk if you want to improve the prefrontal cognitive cortex. Enjoy a new painting vivid in color and improve your visual cortex. Same for auditory cortex, listen to new music. And engaging new smells will improve your olfactory cortex.

What quantum science adds to this are: 1) engage passion in whatever you do; this will help connect to the archetypes and make it much more likely that the meaning you find will be an inspired one. Engaging emotions also makes the new memory extensions more accessible; 2) don't be analytical and digital all the time; consciously engage in holistic processing; this will improve the connections to the right brain; and 3) engage intuitions, archetypes and creativity deliberately: live the do-be-do-be-do way. 4) Make your life purposive and resonant with the evolutionary movement of consciousness. This will force your brain to engage many areas for one task, a sure-fire invitation to the quantum self.

The Awakening of Intelligence

Through the use of creativity, we can make positive noble emotional brain circuits to release the stranglehold of instinctual negative emotions. In this way, the awakening of intelligence can begin to take place in the brain. The choice is yours.

You can live a life of information processor. Alternatively, you can follow the Greek philosopher Epicurus. You will then try to bring "juice" in your life through the pursuit of pleasure: eat, drink, have sex, and be merry. But both lifestyles invariably lead to excess and addiction.

This is low-level intelligence. Higher intelligence is not only to use what you have, what you are born with, but explore what is available to you as your potentiality.

Quantum worldview has good news for you. If you insist on understanding the information to explore your own personal meaning, you are turning on your causal power, your freedom to choose. And it is only the beginning.

Humans have access to infinite new potentialities. It's all there with a caveat: you also have to access your unity consciousness, your "I" to access your infinite new potentiality. You do it through using the mind to process new meaning out of other people's meaning or you own old meaning. You do it by using intuition and follow through exploring the creative process which empirical research and quantum science have completely demystified. You do it by learning to engage your heart. If you are not afraid of the unknown, if you are not afraid of discipline, creativity comes easy. There is ample reward on your way to creatively awaken higher intelligence. This reward is called happiness, increasing levels of happiness as you learn to explore increasing levels of intelligence.

We have a crisis today because we have overdone the separateness. The new science says unequivocally: We need to integrate the mundane and what we call sacred, pleasure and happiness, ego-needs and higher needs, and yes, we can.

The latest brain data is showing that when we integrate, our brain cooperates and changes making more room for more integration.

Ushering in Your New Understanding of the Brain: Stuff to Think about

1. Our first encounter with feeling is in the form of negative emotions. Babies cry; smiles come much later although new mothers like to think otherwise. Think. How do we counter this predominance of negativity from the get-go? Can we?

2. Negative emotions are part of what ancient people used to call evil; some religious people still do. The brave among such people declare: I will conquer the evil. But of course, all they end up doing is to suppress their negative emotions. Think: Is there a better way?

3. Descartes said, "I think, therefore I am." Western philosophers and even lay people ever since have thought of consciousness and thinking as one and the same process. Quantum science forces us to think differently. Consciousness is the ground: physical existence and psyche both are possibilities of consciousness. In view of non-locality, there is no so-called dualism and its interaction problem. How do dual objects, corpus and psyche interact? Dual objects can interact through non-local consciousness. Are you comfortable with these ideas? When you are, the new ways of thinking will empower you.

4. Have you had direct experience of feelings at a chakra, like romantic love in the heart (the feeling is like a tingle or even throb when we are young; as we get old the feeling reduces to just warmth) or what feels like butterflies in your stomach? Reflect on the memories of such experiences.

5. Reflect on cell differentiation in organ-making using the concept of liturgical/morphogenetic fields and how consciousness uses them as blueprints for making epigenetic vital software for the organ-hardware's functional physiology.

6. We have spoken of nine archetypes that are most important for humans to explore: abundance, power, goodness, love, truth, beauty, justice, wholeness, and self. Which one appeals to you the most?

7. Have you ever had an experience of a gut feeling or feeling in your heart about a thought that you somehow cognized to have truth-value? This is an experience of intuition. Reflect on such memories.

8. In the west, they talk about the great chain of being as a hierarchy of body, mind, soul, and spirit. How does quantum science's model of our experiences and hardware-software fit with this depiction?

CHAPTER 3

How Consciousness Uses the Brain to Get a Manifest Self

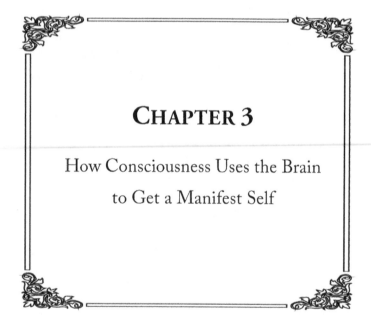

Almost every experimental neurophysiologist or cognitivist, in fact, most people, has an underlying model of perception—how we see an object. An object represents a stimulus field that presents our brain with a stimulus. The brain processes this stimulus, first with the eye and the retina, and then with its higher centers that we will simply call the perception apparatus of the brain. Eventually, an integrated representation of the stimulus/object is made defining an image in a field of the perception apparatus. And it is this image that we see. Simultaneously with perception, the brain makes a memory of the image we see via its memory apparatus.

But many questions thwart any easy validity to this very reasonable physicalist picture. Say, you are looking at a big cat. And you see a big cat, no doubt. However, obviously your brain does not have enough room for a direct representation/image of this "big" cat. So where is this image that you see located?

Furthermore, the representation, the image, must be made of neuronal electrical activity of some sort. How do your neuronal electrical activities add up to an image of a big cat that you actually see? Your neuronal image would be an electrical image of the neuronal field, more like the image of electrons on a TV monitor. In the case of the TV picture, it is easy; your mind gives meaning to the electronic image making it into the meaningful image that you see. Does something similar happen in the case of the brain?

The meaning-giving mind is quantum; brain's perception apparatus acts as a measurement apparatus for the mind and becomes a superposition of possibilities as well. An observer, you, is needed to collapse these possibilities into actuality.

So, how do you the seer arise and where? Are you assuming that there is somehow a TV screen with potentialities of a picture on it (of the external object) in the back of your head and somehow you are looking at it? But if you think of yourself as a homunculus (a little replica of yourself) doing the looking from inside the brain, either you are succumbing to dualism – you are considering yourself separate from the brain – or you get into an infinite regression; however, who is looking at the homunculus to actualize you? Who is looking at the one that is looking at the homunculus? Ad infinitum.

There is still another serious problem with the representation theory. Current sophisticated brain imaging techniques are showing that the perception of an external object sometimes consists of integrating the neuronal activities of many widely separated brain areas. How does the brain bind them together to give us an integral whole that we experience, how do we explain the unity of experience? It smacks of non-locality. This is called the binding problem.

Experts called identity theorists tackle the question of "what do you see?" and "who are you that sees?" simultaneously by positing squarely that in every event of perception you and what you see all come out of the neuronal activity of the involved part of the brain. The experience you have and your brain's neuronal activity are identical. Hence the label: identity theory.

To summarize:

1. If all we experience is sensations in our brain – inside stuff, then why assume outside physical objects at all?

Why not say that there is nothing but me and my cognitions, a philosophy called solipsism? Or, at least the kind of (dualistic) idealism that we mentioned earlier?

2. How can we tell that the neuronal activities of my brain (the representation) really represent an external object if we can never directly see and compare with the object in its suchness?

3. If the objections above seem lethal enough why not posit that I am the brain which directly perceives the object – the identity theory above. This gives us the philosophy of direct realism: external objects are real and the brain directly perceives them without the intermediary of some internal images of them.

4. Also, it is a fact that all our knowledge, about brain and about perception, comes from perception. Is it fair to use knowledge obtained by perception to refute the model above of direct perception? "That would be to cut off the branch on which we sit."

Then, does direct perception make more sense than the representation model? Well, the direct perception model does not explain how the subjective experience of a subject can arise from an object interacting with an object. So, to believe identity theory is to believe that the subject is trivial; that idea that you are a robot with experience once again. But as one theorist puts it this way – "how many identity theorists really believe it or apply it to their own daily lives?" Every scientist we know takes himself or herself very seriously.

There are other serious problems with the direct perception model as well. There are clearly cases where the properties of the representation making capacity of the brain enter. For example, in color perception, is the color a property of the object? Most researchers now think that color is a property of the object as well as that of the brain representation.

And then that question about the mind: How do we see a cat in an electronic image without a meaning-giving mind? In other words, can perception happen without some sort of cognition? Realists do not like the idea of a non-physical mind. Rumor is that one neuroscientist used to joke about this. When asked, "What's mind?" he would say, "Doesn't matter." When asked "What's matter?" he would say, "Never mind."

Ultimately, the philosophical debate between cognitive scientists is one between (dualistic) idealism of a pure brand of representation theorists and the (direct) realism of the identity theorists. Dualistic idealists see the world as primarily ideas. To them perception happens primarily because of what we see inside of us. Realists support direct realism of perception of objects that are outside and real. They want to avoid any reference to objects that are internal like the representations of objects inside the brain.

Pragmatic cognitive neuroscientists are often caught straddling both fences because with the advance of neuroscience they are in a position to study the black box of the brain of behavioral psychology and these studies are giving them (and us) obviously interesting results. But they cannot solve the conceptual quandary of which "ism" is right – (Dualistic) idealism or realism? Philosophically, most cognitive scientists are supporters of realism in the form of material monism. And yet, without some emphasis of "internal" representations, how can they justify their trade?

Quantum physics and quantum measurement theory has given us an integrated alternative: monistic idealism; all experiences arise from one non-local consciousness and its possibilities. Below we will show that this philosophy of monistic, instead of dualistic, idealism can incorporate realism in such a way that offers solution to all the problems of perception.

II The Quantum Measurement Problem and Its Solution

Now is the time to examine the consciousness-based solution of the quantum measurement problem and the observer effect in some detail. Quantum physics says material objects, micro and macro, are waves of possibility; as waves they spread out in various possible positions. But when we measure, we don't see all of these possibilities, an electron smeared over a whole grid of Geiger counters. Instead simply an electron always appears at one or another Geiger counter. Does the Geiger counter change the electron's possibility wave into an actual localized particle? When a micro object, say an electron, impinges upon a whole bunch of Geiger counters, all of which are macro objects made of micro objects, we should logically expect a bigger wave of possibility, instead of an actuality. And yet whenever a human observer is present, the possibilities – electron's and the assembly of the Geiger counters – do change into actualities, a localized particle and the Geiger counter that has "ticked."

According to the context of thinking that I (Amit) was using back in 1981, quantum measurement – change of possibility into actuality – had to be due to some mechanism in the observer's brain. I was a scientific materialist then.

What else is there but the material brain when we think of an observer? We can think of one: consciousness. An observer always looks with self-awareness, the "I" of the observer in addition to the eye (pun intended). But in material monism, consciousness is material brain phenomenon, as well as possibility since the material brain is possibility. You have added one more possibility into the equation, but still no actuality.

On top of all this, the great mathematician John von Neumann's theorem: staying within quantum laws, no material interaction can ever convert possibility into actuality! Go figure.

Von Neumann with great ingenuity did the requisite figuring. The observer's consciousness has to be non-material. Being nonmaterial, consciousness is outside quantum laws and causally effects the event of collapse by choosing among the facets of possibility waves; the chosen facet appears as the particle of actuality.

But the physicist Eugene Wigner pointed out a paradox with von Neumann's thinking. Suppose two observers are simultaneously looking at the same electron with two different Geiger counters. Who gets to choose? Whose choice counts? If both choices count, two Geiger counters at two different places will simultaneously tick; experience contradicts that. If one gets to choose overruling the other because, he is the "head honcho," the problem shifts to: who gets to be head honcho? The paradox remains.

Let's invoke dualistic idealism: consciousness is non-material and consciousness and the material world are separate dual worlds. It is nobody's individual consciousness that chooses, but some bigger consciousness (God?) that chooses among all the possible facets.

One of these dualism thinkers was Bishop Berkeley of the eighteenth century. He was an idealist, a believer of a philosophy that believes things are not real; it is our ideas of consciousness about them that are. There is a paradox about that too! You may have been puzzled over this riddle that causes quite a stir in our consciousness even today: if a tree falls in the forest making a sound but nobody is there to hear it, is there a sound, or not? Berkeley seems to be saying, there should be no sound because there is no person there in the forest with a mind. But of course, this contradicts Newton's laws of cause-effect: if a tree falls, there got to be a sound. So, Berkeley explained: there is always God – consciousness which Berkeley called the mind of God separate from human consciousness, that it is ever present.

So, does quantum collapse happen because of the causal action of an omnipresent God? But this too is paradoxical; if God is always looking, the possibility waves will stay perpetually collapsed. There will be no quantum movement whatsoever! This paradox is called "the watched pot never boils" paradox. But the watched pot does boil as you know; because consciousness actualizes possibilities only in the presence of an observer, and the observer's brain is incapable of looking all the time.

As it happens, in May, 1985, I was talking about all of this with the mystic Joel Morwood, former film-maker. He was the associate producer of a notable film *The Jazz Singer* in the nineteen seventies. I was ranting: if consciousness is brain phenomenon, it is paradoxical; if consciousness is non-material consciousness of the individual, it is paradoxical; if consciousness is (dualistic) God consciousness, it is still paradoxical! What does a quantum physicist have to think of to resolve the paradox?

The rest is history. We had a heated dialogue. At some point, Joel asked, "Is consciousness prior to the brain or brain prior to consciousness?"

To this, I responded smugly (I am the physicist, he is just a film-maker!), "I know all about that. You are talking about non-locality." Indeed, as I have explained before, non-locality defines the domain of quantum potentiality where waves of possibility reside; in this domain communication occurs without signal, and is instantaneous. Naturally this domain is outside space and time; what is prior to what cannot be asked.

Joel was acerbic, "You have scientific blinders on your head," he said. Then he shouted, "There is nothing but God."

Mind you, I have heard those words many times before; they are from Sufism, but all mystics talk like that. As Jesus said, "The kingdom of God is everywhere." And the Upanishads say, *Sarvam Khalydam Brahman* (all is consciousness/Oneness). But this time my internal response was unexpected, a total surprise to myself. I am thinking, suppose consciousness is the ground of being in the domain of potentiality, and matter (including the brain) are possibilities of consciousness itself, what then? An about turn in my thinking! Yes, but who cares? I have solved the measurement problem. The non-local domain of reality that we call potentiality is consciousness – the one and only, inseparable from its possibilities; it splits into a subject in the observer's brain and the object(s) it is looking at upon collapse. All that is needed to start a new paradigm is to identify the non-local domain of potentiality with consciousness itself, the way mystics think, especially in the East.

It was like I was sitting in Plato's cave strapped in a chair so I could look only in front of me and see the shadow show of matter moving in space and time. I had figured out from quantum physics that the shadows are cast by the waves of potentiality. But I could not accommodate the thought that consciousness is casting the shadow by throwing light on the possibility waves, a metaphor for choosing, because of my prejudiced misconceptions about consciousness that I carried in my head. And now I could see the truth because the strap that bound me to look only forward was my own prejudice of material monism. The moment I dropped the prejudice, the straps fell away, I made the about turn and saw the role of consciousness in quantum measurement.

III Tangled Hierarchy: How the Brain Gets its Self

The "I"-experience is not hierarchical. How so? The consciousness-based solution of the quantum measurement problem says this: behold! There are two apparatuses of the brain – perception and memory – both of which contribute to the creation of an entrapment of consciousness in the brain that we call the self. These apparatuses are causally circular. They create (help actualize, that is) each other. This circular causality between two levels of a two-level hierarchy is called a tangled hierarchy. So, our "I", the quantum-self arises from a tangled hierarchy!

Let's fill in some details. The idea that a tangled hierarchy in our brain not only brings about our self but also solves the quantum measurement problem if suitably understood, came to me while I (Amit) was reading artificial intelligence researcher Doug Hofstadter's book *Gödel, Escher, Bach* soon after it came out in 1980. Doug's idea was about building a self-conscious computer program of artificial intelligence and in that field the idea did not pan out. My intuition was that the idea was right for solving the quantum measurement problem.

In our discussion so far, we touched upon the basic solution. Consciousness is the ground of all being; quantum possibilities of matter are possibilities of consciousness itself to choose from. Downward causation is identified as a conscious choice. Consciousness is one and only, so there is no paradox of Wigner's friend.

But the paradox with the observer effect still exists, a circularity that soon raises its ugly head when you ponder deeply. In truth, there is no manifest observer, no observer brain, before the event of collapse. Nobody is looking. But without the observer looking, how can there be actualization?

Materialists tend to miss the true measurement problem: how a measurement produces the subject-object duo. But this real measurement problem has the circularity: No manifest observer, no collapse or actualization; no actualization means there is no manifest observer! Reminds you of a tangled hierarchy, doesn't it?

Indeed, the reason actualization occurs in the presence of an observer's brain but not a Geiger counter is that the brain has a tangled hierarchy in it.

It behooves us now to go into the details of how a tangled hierarchy entraps consciousness and gives the brain a self. By the way, some mystics call this entrapment imprisonment; not an entirely improper description, is it?

Following Hofstadter, consider the liar's sentence, "I am a liar." Notice the circularity. If I am a liar, then I am telling the truth; if I am telling the truth then I am a liar, ad infinitum. The sentence is self-contained, isolated from the rest of the world of sentences. The sentence is also self-referential; it is talking about itself. This is what Hofstadter emphasized.

Now here is the other thing on which we must put emphasis. If you enter the circularity of the sentence and identify with the circularity, you tend to get caught. You think you are embodied in the sentence. Of course, in this case, it is easy for you to get out. After all, it is your tacit acceptance of the rules of the English grammar that got you in. Technically speaking, you belong to the "inviolate level" of implicit English grammar where the sentence cannot go, but you can.

So, the first idea that came to me was this: if the brain has a tangled hierarchical system within it, then when consciousness enters it with the idea of looking at the object(s) through the eyes of the brain and confronted with choosing from its possible facets, it gets caught; the choice actualizes the brain, but consciousness identifies with it and considers itself separate from the other actualized objects the observer is looking at, such as the Geiger counter and the electron. In this way, the observing subject/self and the observed objects co-arise in manifest conscious awareness.

It works. In all events of perception, the perceiver's brain is always one of the objects involved, but the observer never experiences the brain separate from self. The self and the brain are one and the same.

But surely consciousness can also disentangle from the tangled hierarchy just as you can escape from the convoluted logic of the liar's sentence. But what of it? If consciousness disentangles, it is back to the state of one and only, a state that we must now recognize as the unconscious.

The liar's sentence has two levels to make the tangle – the subject and the predicate; what are the two levels of the tangled hierarchy of the brain? One day, I was reading an article by the neuro-philosopher Susan Blackmore in which she points out that perception and memory are a circularly connected pair: perception requires memory to operate and memory requires perception. Blackmore's remark helped me identify the two levels of tangled hierarchy in the brain as the perception and memory apparatuses.

Perception and memory are the dual partners of the brain's tangled hierarchy (fig. 7): there is no memory without perception; there is no perception without memory. The first proposition is obvious; indeed, without perception, no memory. But why do we need memory to create perception?

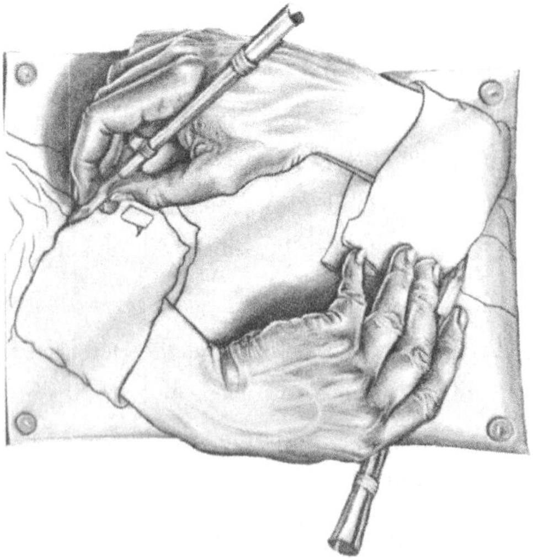

Figure 7. *Drawing Hands* by M.C. Escher. Artist's rendition

Memory is needed to create one-way time, real time. In potentiality, time is a parameter attached to the possibility wave. However, the quantum equation of movement dictates that this parametric time is a two-way street, it can go both ways. But real time is unidirectional, always going toward the future. We need memory to create irreversibility of time, the one way-ness we call time's arrow. This is why memory is needed for the actualization of perception.

One more point. Mystics say that the world of separateness is an appearance. Is this true? Yes, in some real sense. The tangled hierarchy of memory and perception is the same as the tangled hierarchy of Escher's picture of *Drawing Hands* (fig. 7). The left and right hands just appear to create the other locked in an eternal cycle; from behind the scene (the inviolate level), Escher has drawn them both. The same with consciousness (as unconscious) that manifests both the perception and memory apparatuses; they create each other only in appearance, enough to fool immanent consciousness into entrapping itself in a tangled hierarchy.

In order to move forward with this idea, we need to discuss a little history. Indian seers of Vedanta theorized that the force of *maya* created subject-object split of oneness. But the Sanskrit word *maya* also means illusion. This gave rise to an unfortunate philosophy of illusionism (or *mayabad* in Sanskrit) which says, "manifest world is illusory." This had produced confusion in Indian society for generations continuing to this day. In quantum science, *maya* is clearly seen as choice from quantum possibilities; we formally call it downward causation, and all confusion is avoided.

In the West, people are confused from a different perspective. Even quantum aficionados in the West tend to use the phrase "quantum field" instead of conscious choice as the source of downward causation. This perpetuates the notion that even in the quantum worldview the downward causation of consciousness is a force as in Newtonian physics. In quantum physics, only material interactions are forces or force fields, but downward causation is choice; you change another human being via persuasion; force is only required for changing the movement of material objects. When you use force on a human being, you are treating the person as an inanimate object. It is that insensitive, it denies the other's humanity.

Quantum Consciousness and a Paradox-free Theory of Perception

We are not done yet; there are still some other aspects of the paradox of perception mentioned before. When we choose in quantum (un-)consciousness we are operating from non-locality. The choice actualizes the wave of possibility of an object, and also the wave of possibility of our brains. We identify with the brain so collapsed and do not see it as an object. We see the object/stimulus separate from us giving us a "spiritual" experience of immediacy in which the object is seen in its "suchness." That solves one problem mentioned before.

However, if the object/stimulus is one previously experienced or something even remotely similar to what we ordinarily experience, we do not usually recognize this "primary" collapse event. Instead, we see the object upon repeated reflection from the mirror of the past memory, which is subjective and individual. The past memories modulate secondary actualization events so that the perception of the actualized object acquires an individual ego-flavor. This is how the Buddhist doctrine of dependent co-arising works to give us the ego-experience. This is also a factor contributing to the subjectivity of the felt qualia of perception.

The neuroscientist Benjamin Libet's experiments show that the processing time of secondary collapses is about 500 milliseconds or thereabouts (read chapter 6 for details). When we finally recognize the object, we are quite acquainted with our past memory that we have just sifted through, we are in our ego-self ("me") have been conditioned by these memories, giving us the self of individuality.

How about that television-image-in-an-inner theater aspect of the representation theory discussed before? We have been forgetting something so far. Along with the external physical object and the observer's brain there is something else that quantum consciousness actualizes routinely – the meaning that mind gives to the observation. The brain's representations of the stimulus are literally brain neuronal states of electrical activity, no doubt. They are not unlike the electronic movement on a TV screen. But we do not see the electronic patterns when we watch TV, do we? Instead, our mind gives meaning to the Rorschach of fluorescent spots on the screen produced by the electronic movement. Similarly, in the case of perception, our mind gives a quantum superposition of possible meanings to the neuronal potentialities of electrical image of the brain representation. Eventually, it is our mind that produces the possible recognizable images of the object of perception from the current neuronal representation as modulated by the previous memory, possibilities for consciousness to choose from. Hence, there is no perception without cognition.

Optical Illusions

Let's discuss optical illusions. Our minds giving meaning is what makes illusion possible. For example, take the case of the famous cartoon that W. E. Hill created (fig 8), *My Wife and My Mother-in-Law*. You begin with seeing one meaning, either the wife or the mother in law. Then you experiment with changing your perspective of looking by shifting your head this way or that way. You are looking at the same lines, but the perspective from which you look changes the brain's electrical configuration and the mind gives it different meanings. You see the other picture.

Figure 8. *My wife and my mother-in-law*, by W. E. Hill. Artist's rendition.

And nowhere is the meaning-giving necessity for the mind clearer than how we see the so-called moon illusion: the horizon moon looks bigger to us than an overhead moon. If you take a picture with a camera, the difference of size of the horizon moon from the overhead moon disappears. If the brain were like a camera, then you would not see the illusion, but you do. Your mind constructs the illusion since an object perceived across a large terrain – the horizon moon – is also interpreted by your mind to be at larger distance than the overhead moon seen through empty space. And so, mind makes the horizon moon look bigger just as it makes the upper rectangle in fig. 9 look bigger. The latter is called the size illusion.

Figure 9. The size illusion. The upper rectangle looks bigger. The reason the upper rectangle and the horizon moon looks bigger is similar: in both cases, mind illusorily thinks they are further away, and therefore compensates and make them look bigger.

What if there is no previous memory of the object we are looking at, nothing even remotely close? There is a story about Columbus and his crew as they landed in the "new world". The natives asked them, "How did you come?" The sailors said, "On our ships of course." And they pointed to the sea where the ships were. But the natives could not see them, not immediately. Indeed, it would be hard to "see" something *really* new!

The oneness of experience of the binding problem is also solved in the quantum model of perception. Because consciousness is fundamentally non-local, it can bind together all the different areas of the brain making up the perception apparatus to produce one unified brain state of actualization.

And you know what! Brain scientists are demonstrating that this is indeed the case. When such a binding takes place and different areas of the brain act in synchrony, the result is a brain gamma wave of 40 Hz oscillation called a gamma burst signifying the onset of the quantum-self-experience.

So, the final solution of the quantum measurement problem based on quantum physics and monistic idealism as presented here combines the best of realism and (dualistic) idealism, best of direct realism and representation theories of perception/cognition. At the same time, it explains the suchness experiences that are denied in the Western philosophical tradition but that have long been recognized as spiritual experiences in all of the major spiritual traditions, It solves the binding problem. The theory also explains qualia of normal perception. And, of course, the problem of subject-object split nature of awareness and the ego-modality of normal perception are also explained.

Broadly speaking, quantum measurement theory based on primacy of consciousness solves the following long-standing paradoxes and problems of science:

1. The quantum measurement paradox.
2. The biological paradox of how to distinguish between non-life and life.
3. The paradox of perception of cognitive science.
4. The paradox of the one way-ness of time, a paradox of physics and philosophy.

5. The paradox of wisdom traditions – how the One becomes many.

In science, it is customary to value theories that solve problems of many different fields of scientific research in one fell-swoop; Readers, please note.

There is a newspaper cartoon called *Bizarro* in which the cartoonist thought of a bizarre scene of a woman dating with a brain in a vat, no kidding. The woman is seen to be complaining, "When you said in your email that you are a real brain, I thought you meant you're really smart."

Interestingly, the neuroscientist Jonathon Harrison had already created for us the interesting case of Ludwig, a brain in a vat, to ponder. In his scenario, Ludwig, who was born with a great brain but a deformed body, was "rescued" by a surgeon named Dr Smythson. This surgeon removed Ludwig's brain from his ugly body and kept it functioning with a life support system. The cut ends of Ludwig's cranial nerves, spinal cord and all that were connected to complex cybernetic systems of such capacity that Ludwig's brain could continue to be stimulated in exactly the way it was before via sense organs and external stimuli. Dr Smythson did not forget to connect the cut ends of the motor nerves and the "sensory" input so that Ludwig also experienced the so-called free-willed movements like raising your arm when you will it. So in effect, Ludwig, a brain in a vat so to speak, was able to have all the experiences of a normal human life, like eating a meal, sleeping, thinking about philosophy, having a love life, whatever the good surgeon cared to simulate, including all the usual experiences of a normal life with a real physical body.

So, Harrison raised the question: How do we know that we are not brains in a vat? It seems that we do not know, we *cannot* know!

You can see that this is the same argument that seems to justify the dualistic idealism that Bishop Berkeley proposed. The truth is, all local experiences can be simulated. Today, we can readily imagine constructing a computer-generated virtual reality that can replace our local reality, the same idea as Harrison's.

This has given us the notion that many neuroscientists are openly propagating. We could be p-robots or if you prefer p-zombies, "p" stands for philosophical. You are philosophically different from a robot because, the neuroscientists concede, you have experiences, which the robot can never have. But your experiences have no causal power; they cannot disturb anything in the universe, so they make no difference.

So, what is the way out of this kind of paradox, if it is a paradox at all? For a monistic idealist with the kind of theory of perception/cognition that we have constructed above, there is no paradox. Computers can simulate everything that is local, but nothing that is non-local; the physicist Richard Feynman made that point long ago, in a scientific paper published in 1981. So, Ludwig's so-called simulated life would entirely consist of local experiences which are strictly material. The non-local mixture that gives us the spark of life, like the oceanic feelings of love, would be completely lacking. Also, even the ordinary thoughts of pondering casually about meaning and similar other feelings cannot be simulated by machines.

Are you a p-robot? An episode of *Star Trek*, the TV series will help you answer. The series spins stories of a twenty-third century human society where usual punishments are non-existent. And yet, people are not transformed; the Star Trek authors could not imagine that. So, the people still commit crime. In one episode, some man commits a crime and what punishment does he get? To spend rest of his life in the company of many beautiful women! There is only one catch. All the women are androids, robots.

No man would ever prefer having many beautiful android women to one human woman I reckon, not even a materialist scientist. Would he? He would get his "tea," but no empathy. So, it indeed was a punishment.

Cognitive neuroscientists work with the idea of making mind science more objective, a goal towards which they have made considerable progress, for example, magnetic resonance imaging (MRI) of thoughts or the more advanced functional fMRI where they also measure blood flow and oxygen levels in the various parts of the brain simultaneously.

Here is a quick explanation of how fMRI works. Most of the atoms in the human body and brain are hydrogen atoms with a positively-charged proton in its nucleus. When the MRI machine emits a magnetic field, these protons align with the magnetic field. When radio waves pulse into the patient's brain, the protons are thrown out of alignment. As the protons resort back into their original alignment (a movement called precession) they produce a radio signal back. The time and amount of re-alignment changes depending on the thickness and hardness of the tissue. The radio waves emitted from the protons in this way produce a clear image of the brain. In the 1900s, another physicist discovered that the effect of the magnetic field depends on how rich in oxygen the blood in the brain organ is. This gives away the secret of what brain organs are active.

We have come full circle with our consciousness-based approach. The lesson of this chapter is that we cannot reconcile perception itself with cognitive neuroscience without firmly founding it within the metaphysics of the primacy of consciousness, or monistic idealism, and without giving value to what is internal such as mental thoughts about meaning.

So, it is time to rest the battle of supremacy between external and internal and recognize that science needs both. An MRI image of thought does not give the scientist any clue for the meaning content of thought, for which an inter-subjective dialogue between the scientist and the subject of the thought is essential.

Will cognitive neuroscience still be science if subjective experiences of meaning are allowed to enter it as valid data? Yes, so long as the criterion of weak objectivity is kept in mind. Data should never be allowed if it is subject-specific. But if the data is independent of a specific subject, if it is basically the same for many subjects, it passes muster.

As the physicist Bernard d'Espagnat argued some time ago in a book called *In Search of Reality*, quantum physics supports weak objectivity. Strictly speaking, measurements of individual events cannot be replicated in quantum experiments, only the measurements of many events on the average.

The Stability of Our Perceptual World Is the Gift of Our Mind

When things get hectic, we all sometimes wonder, "There is so much happening." Brain scientists will tell you, "You don't know even a thousandth of it." It is true. In an ever-changing world, our brains must receive tons and tons of information creating tons and tons of potentialities for consciousness to process. Consciousness uses its mind and mind's meaning-giving capacity to significantly pare down the possibilities to choose from. In this way, it is the mind and meaningfulness that gives us a perceptual world that has a fair amount of stability.

Out of all the complex sensory data that the brain processes, our consciousness operates on the simple principle of seeing the simplest meaningful picture. As a car moves further away, it makes smaller and smaller images on the retina. Do we wonder if we are seeing a different car, a whole series of smaller and smaller cars? No. Instead we perceive that the car is moving away from us, which is the simplest available meaning.

Unconscious Perception

Unconscious perception is a class of phenomena that causes cognitive dissonance in many people because of the unfortunate choice of words – how can one perceive but have no consciousness of it? Well, the unconscious does not mean that there isn't consciousness. In monistic idealism, consciousness is the ground of being; where would it go? In the unconscious, there is consciousness, but no awareness. Unconscious perception is perception without awareness. It proves that things do go on in the unconscious, namely, possibilities interact with possibilities producing new possibilities.

Evidence abounds for such phenomena. There is a phenomenon called blind sight in which people who have lost their normal cortical vision (but the pathways for vision through the midbrain remain intact) clearly can sense obstacles or distinguish between patterns beyond chance coincidence and yet claim unawareness of sight. Similarly, if a picture of a bee is flashed very fast before a subject, the subject does not have conscious awareness of the picture, and yet a subsequent association test elicits words such as honey or sting, suggesting that they indeed perceived the bee after all.

Another very important data was gathered with experiments performed on split brain patients whose corpus callosum is severed. One such woman was shown a picture of a nude male model in her left visual field which is processed by the right brain. She blushed but didn't know why; this shows that seeing with the right brain is unconscious vision.

This is all convincing data proving the importance of thinking of neuroscience in the new context of the primacy of consciousness. However, the most convincing data is the transferred potential between two correlated brains.

VI The Grinberg Transferred Potential Experiment

The most important prediction of the quantum theory of brain's self is that the brain's perception apparatus better be a quantum system. If it is, we can verify this by showing light flashes to one observer producing brain activity and check if this brain activity can be transferred to another observer's brain without any electrical connection. This would have to be a transfer via the non-locality of the unity consciousness since we have eliminated communication via the local signals of electromagnetism.

You already know the game changing concept. Contrary to spiritual expectation, the unity consciousness between individuals is only a potentiality. How do we actualize the unity, "correlate" them or "entangle" them? The experiments with submicroscopic objects show that it is pretty easy to correlate them into oneness. We just have to allow them to come close and interact. Then, even if they move far away, they remain correlated.

But how do we correlate two perception apparatuses in two individual brains into oneness? I (Amit) did write a scientific paper on consciousness and quantum measurement and published it in a physics journal called *Physics Essays* in 1989. Imagine the odds, but a Mexican neurophysiologist was aware of my work. And I got a call from him even before my book *The Self-Aware Universe* was published carrying much more details.

"Professor Goswami, my name is Jacobo Grinberg. I am a neurophysiologist at the University of Mexico. My students and I have done some experiments and I think you would be interested in our results," the man at the other end of the telephone said.

"Tell me more," I said.

"Well, we have demonstrated, I think, the non-local transfer of information between brains. I also think, your theory predicts that. So, you should see our data and tell us what you think."

Amazing, I thought, catching the gist of what he was saying. You know, I confess that I had not thought of this possibility before; if I had done so, then I myself would have predicted this non-local information transfer between brains, and the paper I published would have been better for it. So, this Jacobo Grinberg must be an extraordinary scientist, I thought. Naturally, I said:

"Dr Grinberg, I would love to see the data. This is super."

And thus it was arranged that I would go to Mexico City and meet Jacobo Grinberg and his collaborators at the University of Mexico. There I checked out his laboratory, saw an experiment done before my eyes and the data analyzed.

How did Jacobo correlate two brains? His protocol was this. Two subjects meditated together with the intention that they will have direct, that is signal-less and non-local, communication. For the first twenty minutes, the subjects meditated in proximity. For the rest of the experiment though, they meditated in isolation in individual electromagnetically insulated Faraday cages while their scalps were wired with electrodes that connected their brain to individual EEG machines. One subject was shown a series of light flashes; the other subject no such light flashes. Yet when their brain wave data were examined upon eliminating noise and a signal extracted, both data showed remarkable similarity in strength and phase. The data is understandable for the subject who saw light flashes. Light flashes do activate the occipital area of the brain and the resultant electrical activity has been known to produce brain waves measurable by an EEG. The signal output of the EEG is called the evoked potential. But how did the electrical activity make it to the other observer while he or she is sitting in electromagnetic isolation and produce a clear "transferred" potential (fig. 10)? Indeed, control subjects, people who did not meditate together or could not hold the intention for the duration of experiment never exhibited any transferred potential (fig. 10).

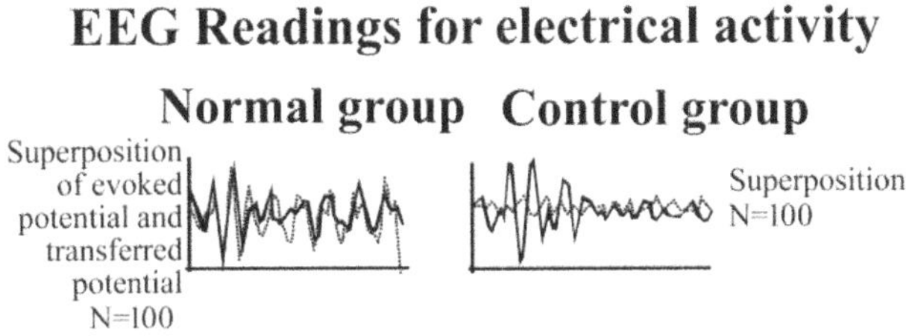

Figure 10. (a) The transferred potential between people of meditative intention; (b) control subjects (no meditation) do not show transferred potential.

Later that week, Jacobo and I wrote the now famous paper (co-authored with Leah Attie and another post-doctoral associate of Jacobo, M. Delaflor) on transferred potential – transfer of electrical activity from one human subject's brain to that of another without the exchange of signals just because the two subjects meditated with the intention of direct signal-less communication during the duration of the experiment.

The night we finished the paper, Jacobo took me to his hideout (that's how he described it) in the forest near his house which was a little outside of the city. We talked for several hours. I don't remember much details of that conversation, since it has been more than two decades, (this was in 1992) except for this exchange:

I said with no little tremor in my voice, "You know Jaco, we are witnessing and writing about the first definitive machine-measured scientific evidence for the existence of God." Jacobo looked back at me and smiled, but did not say anything. But he didn't have to; the way he received my words, the way his eyes grew large, I had no doubt that he completely agreed with my assessment.

In the subsequent two decades plus, there have been some two dozen experiments replicating Jacobo Grinberg's data; so, there is no doubt about the veracity of the transferred potential experiment or the quantum nature of the brain's perception apparatus.

In an earlier era, neuroscientists used to look for a seat for the self, akin to a computer command center, the central processing unit.

Here is an example. In coma or a cerebral concussion, neuroscientists found that an organ in the brain stem, quite centrally located called the reticular formation, goes out of commission. Also, brain-affecting drugs like LSD act on the brain stem including the reticular formation. So, a theory was proposed: the reticular formation is where awareness arises. This is the CPU, the command center.

Neuroscientists also used to try to find models of the self by studying pathologies. If the pathology of a brain organ directly affects our sense of the self, it seems rational to see a connection. There is a pathology that affects our awareness of the body image; so, a neuroscientist of some repute speculated that the parietal lobe responsible for our body image must be the site of the self.

But since then, more realization has dawned. Awareness is sometimes the result of more holistic actions in the part of the brain – when many brain areas are involved in a synchronous integrative manner. It is no CPU that can give us such non-local awareness.

You can think of each of these brain areas pulsating, vibrating producing music. Can the music be phase coherent? To be so, they have to vibrate with the same frequency, which is not likely. It is much easier is to imagine that they vibrate in synchrony. But then in an actual orchestra, we need a conductor to maintain synchrony. Where is the conductor? There is the specter of CPU again!

Staunch materialists have one more option: complexity theory. Brain's complexity is responsible for all its miraculous actions. It is based on the philosophy of emergent epiphenomenalism: the self is an emergent epiphenomenon of the neocortex except that this theory is highly mathematical.

The post-materialist solution given by quantum science as discussed in the last chapter is to evoke quantum physics and the primacy of consciousness. If the different brain areas oscillate in place as in musical instruments, they are quantum, and they become correlated by neuronal signals transmitted via the glial cells (the white matter in the brain; so far what we have talked about all consists of grey matter), then consciousness binds them together via its non-locality forming a trap called the tangled hierarchy. And in the process of quantum measurement, consciousness, trying to look through the brain, gets caught in the trap and splits itself into two: a subject looking at an object. We call it co-arising.

Brain Evidence for the Quantum Self: The 40 Hz Oscillation

The evoked potential mentioned above is related to the light flashes that the subject was shown; for that reason, it is also referred to as event-related potential, ERP in abbreviation. Brain wave data, for many years, have been revealing the P300 potential, recorded on the scalp 300 milliseconds after the event/stimulus. This is usually considered as an unconscious event which is however a precursor of conscious events such as verbal reports some few hundred milliseconds later. In a paper written with Jacobo Grinberg many years ago but published only recently, I (Amit) had speculated that this P300 ERP got to be associated with the primary perception of the quantum self and the latter what neuroscientists call the conscious event is associated with our conditioned ego.

More recently, neuroscientists have learnt how to put microelectrodes deep inside the brains of epileptic patients. This has given us a surprise. These measurements by microelectrodes reveal a sudden burst of approximately 40 hertz oscillation (called a gamma brain wave) immediately following the P300. This is the signature of conscious awareness of the primary quantum self. Why? This is because, apparatuses in distant areas of the brain are simultaneously communicating in synchrony which confirms quantum non-locality.

The famous biologist Francisco Varela seems to agree with me. In a report to the Dalai Lama about recent progress of neuroscience he said this:

When we perform a cognitive act, for example, we have a visual perception, the perception is not a simple fact of an image in the retina. There are many, many sites in the brain that become active. The big problem, Your Holiness, is how these many, many active parts become coherent to form a unity. When I see you, the rest of my experience, my posture, my emotional tone, is all a unity. It is not dispersed, with perception here and movement there.

How does that happen? Imagine that each one of the sites in the brain is like a musical note. It has a tone. Why a tone? Empirically, there is an oscillation. The neurons in the brain oscillate all over the place. Each goes whoomph and then ffhhh. The woomph is when different places in the brain oscillate, and these become harmonized. When you have a wave here, a wave there, from different parts of the brain, several become harmonized, so they oscillate together.

When the brain sets into a pattern, to have a perception, or to make a movement, the phase of these oscillations become harmonized, what we call phase-locked. The waves oscillate together in synchrony…

Many patterns of oscillations in the brain spontaneously select each other to create the melody; that is the moment of experience. That is the whoomph. But the music is created with no orchestra conductor. This is fundamental.

You don't have a little man there saying, "Now you, and you, and you."

(Quoted in an article by David Goleman in the anthology, *Measuring the Immeasurable*, pp 202-203)

How is the symphony in the brain happening spontaneously? Consciousness is identifying with the brain while trying to see the external object through it, and getting captured in the brain's tangled hierarchy and becoming the quantum self. Only the quantum measurement theory as elucidated in the previous pages can explain that. What arises as the subject we call the quantum self but Varela and the Dalai Lama, being Buddhists, would call it no-self.

The Dalai Lama is now a strong advocate of the importance of the quantum worldview in consciousness research. "No worldview of reality is complete without quantum physics", said he in April 2017. We hope you will agree. And even materialist neuroscientists will follow suit someday.

Can the Brain's Perception apparatus be quantum?

Still the idea that the brain has a quantum self, stretches the average scientist's credibility because to him "obviously," the brain is a macroscopic material machine at room temperature and according to usual conceptualization, its quantum behavior should give way to Newtonian behavior for all practical purpose. And yet, without quantum behavior or non-locality, how would we explain different components of the brain oscillating in synchrony? How would we explain the transferred potential between two correlated brains?

Neuroscientists just ignore the transferred potential data. Years ago, I mentioned this data to Dr Ramachandran, a neuroscientist of considerable reputation, at a conference at Deepak Chopra's wellness center. He said he would look into it; that it is very interesting, but he has given no official response that I have seen.

Some quantum scientists keep trying to prove that although it is a macro body operating at a relatively high room temperature, the brain somehow is a quantum object. The most well-known of these claims is the work of Stanford scientist Peter Hammeroff, who in collaboration with the famous Roger Penrose gave us the idea that a living cell's microtubules have something to do with the quantum nature of the brain and consciousness. But the work has not found experimental corroboration for its basic assumptions, and Penrose's contribution to the theory vainly assumes that consciousness is an object.

But of course, we have been forgetting something! We said in chapter 2 about how every material living body, a cell or tissue, or organ comes with correlated functional software whose origin can be traced back to liturgical/morphogenetic fields whose movements are quantum. So, every living object is quantum because it measures quantum liturgical fields to make its vital correlate. Consciousness does have access to all living objects; you can correlate living objects in potentiality with each other because of this. We will give further details in the next chapter.

So, in summary, we cannot fully understand the brain's capacity to perceive or have a self without introducing mental meaning and vital feeling in our dynamics. Perception is always perception/cognition either with feeling or with meaning.

Questions to Ponder Upon

1. There is no sense perception without cognition. Why? And why is this a good thing? Wonder about all the little things that work together that enables us to experience the world in a sensible way.
2. In this chapter, you are seeing how deep the problem of quantum measurement takes us. To the materialist physicist, it is a paradox by itself; to the cognitive scientist similarly the problem of perception is a paradox; for the psychologist, the relation of mind and brain is a paradox; to the mystic, how the One becomes two is a paradox; to the biologist how to differentiate between life and non-life is a paradox; to the philosopher, the unidirectional nature of time is a paradox. To a quantum physicist, all these paradoxes have the same solution. Not only that, the solution leads to a viable science of consciousness. While scientists and mystics remain compartmentalized within their respective fields, you dear reader, don't have to. You can ponder the deep wisdom of quantum measurement theory and integrative thinking.

3. Ponder over the transferred potential experiment and why this is an experimental demonstration for the existence of God (as Oneness consciousness).

4. Ancient seers did not know about quantum physics or non-locality. But nevertheless, they postulated that consciousness (which they call the causal level, *karana sharira* in Sanskrit) uses the subtle levels (the vital and the mental, *sukhshma sharira* in Sanskrit) to connect to the gross level of matter (*sthula sharira*). Ponder over this wisdom which we are verifying after seven thousand years.

CHAPTER 4

How Your Brain Gets its Negative Emotional Software

When I (Amit) was in college, I used to joke with friends at the adjacent medical school about how hard their life must be with all those anatomical names to remember. In fact, in those days, I often felt blessed that I did not enroll in the medical school.

What happened was this. My mother very much wanted me to become a medical doctor. So, I put in an application. And of course, I got admission and there was even the assurance of a scholarship. All good? Well, no. When I went to register, the nauseating thought of having to dissect cadavers changed my mind. Instead, I registered in the adjacent liberal arts college and became a student of physics.

But then, look at the irony. After all these years in physics, I got into the meaning questions of quantum physics which brought me to consciousness research which brought me to brain anatomy. Talking about bad karma!

Dear reader. If you feel the way I do when you read a brain book out of the good will prompted by curiosity about yourself and self-improvement, I will tell you how I learned to bypass the intricacies of brain anatomy and you can too. The brain is a complex composite of many organs each with well-defined organ functions. Most brain books start with the entire picture of brain anatomy with all those complicated organ names. Big mistake. The trick is to pare it down to the essentials in a need-based way. The details can come only when you need them. Of course, it helps when you have an experienced doctor with the same curiosity nearby to help you in your search.

So far, we have mentioned the neocortex—that's the top layer of the brain where the ego-self arises. We have also spoken of the midbrain or limbic brain where the negative emotional brain circuits are. Additionally, we introduced a picture of the brain that the brain researcher Paul Mclean called the tripartite brain consisting of three concentric shells (see fig. 1 a). Mclean theorized that the brain evolved layer by layer. First, the innermost shell: the reptilian brain, also called the R-complex. Then evolved the mammalian brain or the limbic midbrain (so named because it looks like limbs around the innermost layer). And finally, the top layer – the neocortex came into the picture with the evolution of higher primates and humans.

The important organ for the reptile brain is the thalamus. In the middle layer, the important organs are: basal ganglia which are bundles of neurons, the amygdala, the hypothalamus, and the hippocampus. For the top layer – cerebral cortex or neocortex – the important organs can be broadly classified as motor cortex, sensory cortex and association cortex. It is also common to see the neocortex in terms of lobes – the frontal lobe, the parietal lobe, the temporal lobe, the occipital lobe and so on (see fig .1 b).

And of course, you already know one more important thing: the three shells of the brain are symmetrically split into the left and right hemispheres; in other words, there are left and right neocortices, left and right midbrains, and left and right thalamuses.

Finally, imagine that all these three shells straddle the brain stem, which is not divided between left and right hemispheres and which is really an outgrowth of the spinal cord. Got it? This should be simple enough for a starter.

Next, let's make an alphabetical list for you of all the important brain apparatuses and their functions that is referred to in the book.

Important Brain Organs and Their Functions

Accumbens: A nucleus in the pleasure area of the midbrain.

Anterior cingulate cortex (ACC): A cingulate indicates a curved bundle of nerves. This organ directs rational thinking such as making plans. Developing this area helps balance thinking and feeling, helps develop emotional intelligence.

Amygdala: Responds to emotionally charged stimuli and in this way helps direct the instinctual negative emotional brain circuits.

Basal ganglia: Ganglia indicate a bundle of nerves. This bundle is part of the pleasure/reward circuit.

Brain stem: Contains brain's arousal system and sends neurotransmitters such as dopamine and norepinephrine to the rest of the brain.

Caudet nucleus: An organ of the pleasure and reward system.

Cerebellum: The regulator of movement.

Corpus callosum: Mediates the information transfer between the brain's two hemispheres.

Hippocampus: This organ makes new memory and puts sequence to memory making.

Hypothalamus: Regulates primal drive of hunger and sexual appetite, and directs the pituitary gland.

Limbic brain: The emotional mid-brain.

Parietal lobe: This is where our somatosensory cortex is and where the physical body image is formed.

Pituitary gland: Controls the hormones of the body such as cortisol. Also makes endorphins.

Prefrontal cortex: This is the seat of the ego-self and its decision-making and also of the intellect.

Thalamus: Relay station of sensory stimuli.

Ventral tegmental area (VTA): Part of the pleasure and reward areas of the midbrain.

From the quantum measurement theory, we learn that it is the brain's different regions that give us the capacity of sense perception and memory and that enables a material brain to acquire a self that seems to experience the world separate from itself. Brain's perception and memory apparatuses make a tangled hierarchy, that's how. From what we know about a single living cell, it too has both capacities of perception and memory. Even a single cell can distinguish between itself and the environment; in other words, it can sense the environment as separate from itself. A living cell can also remember what objects of the environment are friendly (food) and what are the enemy (poison) once it encounters them a few times. So, manifest consciousness or awareness – subject-object split – is present even in a living cell. We can also surmise that manifest consciousness began on earth with the creation of a single living cell.

A living cell has something else: programmed molecules – DNA and protein. DNA is the hereditary molecule; portions of DNA are called genes and genes have the genetic code or program to make proteins. Proteins have built-in programs to carry out purposive cellular functions. Where are the perception and memory making capacities of a cell located? The biologist Bruce Lipton claims that the cell wall has the requisite proteins for perception. There is memory-making capacity in the water of the cytoplasm.

Molecules are governed by physical laws, no doubt about that. Physical laws are causal laws. What brings purpose to the cellular molecules and the cell itself? Consciousness does, when it chooses it chooses with purpose. Choosing from quantum possibilities of liturgical/morphogenetic blueprints, consciousness programs purposive biological functional software in the macromolecules of the living cell, the water in the cytoplasm, the cell wall, and the cell itself, as a whole.

To summarize, every cell, every composite of cells that we call an organ that carries out a purposive function is correlated or entangled in the quantum way to become one with its liturgical blueprints of function. Every organ has a V-organ, the name we give to its vital correlate, associated with it (see fig. 5). The feeling of vitality the cell experiences, that vital energy comes from the movement of the blueprint.

What do cells cognize with, give interpretation to sensing? They cognize with feelings. Indeed, until the neocortex comes into the evolutionary picture, all living composites of cells, plants and animals, cognize with feelings.

So basically, what is the distinction between the living and the non-living? The differences are:

- Living beings has a manifest self, an embodiment of consciousness itself.
- A living being has experiences of vital energy movements or simply feelings that allow it cognition – knowing.
- Living beings without a neocortical brain cognize only with sensing and feeling. Since a cell always comes as physical-vital pair, sensing would always come mixed up with feeling in the living experience all the way up in the evolutionary ladder.
- All this changes when we develop an additional way of cognizing – thinking, along with a thinking self.

> When the thinking self appears on the scene, it more or less overpowers all the feeling selves which are then largely suppressed from our experience.

Objects of feeling are quantum. I (Valentina) have for a long time studied the old Chinese wise concepts. These Chinese figured out this quantum nature of vital energy long ago empirically, of course; they did not call it that way, how could they, the concept was not around. The Chinese called energies of feeling *chi* and they have been studying *chi* for millennia. From the get-go, they noticed that feelings have two aspects: one (creative) aspect is revealed in stillness – they call it *yin*; and the second is a dynamic (conditioned) aspect that manifests in action and they call it *yang*. You can of think of *yin* as the wave mode of *chi* (potentiality) and *yang* as the particle mode (actuality).

This yin-yang dichotomy is no superfluous thinking. It led to the development of a very successful medicine system called Traditional Chinese Medicine (TCM). Today, who hasn't undergone at least one bout of acupuncture treatment to relieve pain? Acupuncture is part of TCM.

The important thing is that because of their quantum nature, vital liturgical fields can be correlated with other vital liturgical fields. And you can experience another person's feeling through this correlation that gives oneness and non-local communication. There is much evidence that plants can pick up your feelings as can animals like your pet dog. How are they doing it? Non-locally, of course, via the mediation of consciousness.

So, all living beings are quantum at either level, a single cell or a conglomerate of cells forming an organ, because a quantum vital blueprint is needed to program function in that cell or conglomerate of cells.

Let's spell out once more the differences between the Newtonian model of brain organs that the establishment neuroscientists subscribe to and the new quantum view of the same organs where the correlation with the liturgical/morphogenetic fields provides them with quantum nature. When two Newtonian organs interact in the Newtonian way, they remain separate as they interact. In the quantum view, the local interaction actualizes the unity of the two organs via the mediation of consciousness. When several organs of the brain, thus unified, participate in the quantum dance, the music they create becomes harmonious. This harmony is the numinosity of the quantum self that we experience when the tangled hierarchical collapse of the perception and memory apparatuses actualize the experience.

Quantum Measurement in the Brain and Qualia

Let's go back to one thorny issue of quantum measurement problem that we left unfinished in the last chapter, the issue of "felt" experience. We assert that the perception organ in our brain is quantum not because the physical organ is, which is much arguable, but because it measures the vital blueprints—the liturgical fields; the actualization leads to not only sensing but also feeling.

Now you can fully understand felt qualia – the concept of felt experience in connection with subjectivity. Every sensory experience of the brain comes with a subjective feeling giving us that felt qualia of experience.

Neuroscientists theorize that evolution has given us instinctual unconscious memory in the form of the brain's neuronal circuits in organs in the midbrain, the amygdala and adjacent pleasure areas the VTA. When we see a suitable stimulus connected with our survival, the functional motif of the first two chakras, this unconscious memory is activated producing response that are jokingly referred to as the four F's – fleeing, fighting, feeding, and f-king – but they are no jokes. These responses are more often than not interpreted by the mind as negative emotions – fleeing corresponds to fear; fighting is response of the negative emotion of aggression, anger, violence, competitiveness, or domination; feeding maybe a response to the negative emotion of greed, and f-ing to the negative emotion of lust. Notice that for animals without a mind, these instincts are just pure feelings, and are necessities for survival. Our negativity associated with the feelings is a contribution of the human mind.

Clearly, during evolution the limbic brain has taken over the feelings at the first two chakras. Recent research has also uncovered other interesting data that suggest that the brain may control even the immune and gastrointestinal systems of our body. New fields of research – psychoneuroimmunology and psycho-neuro-gastro-intestinology – have been created around this new data.

Let's talk about Ader's experiment, the research that led to the creation of psychoneuroimmunology. Bob Ader was working on a Pavlovian conditioning experiment of teaching rats the aversion towards saccharine-flavored water. The standard practice was to correlate the rats' drinking of water with the taking of a drug (psychophosphamide) via injection, a drug that induces nausea and vomiting. Rats quickly learned to associate the sweet water with the nausea. After the conditioning, the rats would have nausea with just sweet water; the drug was not needed any more. But there was a peculiar complication. The rats also seemed to have learnt to die quickly as a result of drinking sweet water. Ader discovered that the drug had a side effect: it induced a suppression of the immune system. As a result of the conditioning using the drug, the rats had not only learned to simulate (upon drinking sweet water) the nauseating effect of the drug but also the immune suppression effect. It was the permanent suppression of the immune system that made the rats prone to disease and death.

Experiments soon followed even at the human level. One of the first such studies correlated the infection rate of sailors while on board of a ship with their actual life events. The sailors who were the unhappiest as a result of their life events were also found to have the highest rate of infection. Perceived negative meaning produces emotional stress which in turn produces immune system disorder – a clear case of psychoneuroimmunology.

The brain can influence the immune system, through nerves and through molecules of neuropeptide. Similar experiments make a case for psycho-neuro-gastro-intestinology. Brain can influence the gastrointestinal systems (of the root and the navel chakras).

A reasonable hypothesis then would be that brain takes over the control of the functions of the organs at all the body chakras. This is why it seems like we never experience pure feelings but always feelings mixed with thoughts, a combination we called emotions.

Do we experience pure feelings in the brain at all?

Our self-identity is associated with the sixth brow chakra to be sure. And indeed, although the organs at this chakra, the neocortex, is mainly for thinking, we do feel clarity when we understand something, and confusion when we don't. So, there is a self that feels here as well. However, these feelings naturally get mixed with thoughts which are the chakra's main function and what we experience are emotions. So, again the question, can we, or do we experience pure feelings in the brain?

The amygdala, which is certainly involved with emotions in the brain, is not part of the neo-cortex. Does the amygdala, the mid-brain have a self which is largely unconscious in us overwhelmed by the cortical self?

A related question arises here. Most mammals do not have a neocortex. Do they have a self? Do they feel at all at organ level?

Mammals have the mid-brain, the middle shell of the brain that sits on the hind brain like limbs. Some mammals can be domesticated; for example, our pets like dogs and cats. Anyone who has a mammalian pet will say this: these pets have feelings at a much more enhanced level than, for example, a plant, an octopus, or a snake. How do these pets feel so strongly? Do they have a self at the midbrain?

Now let's recall that self-identity has a requirement: tangled hierarchy of a cognition apparatus and a memory apparatus: the circular nature of perception and memory. It is easy to see that the mid-brain has both capacities in the organs of amygdala and hippocampus.

We submit that there is a chakra with a feeling self at the midbrain. For mammals, especially pets, there is subject-object collapse: this self enables mammals to feel the vital energies at the mid-brain. This is what created the instinctual brain circuits in the mammalian brain.

For us humans, the neocortical thinking-self obscures the feeling-self at the midbrain so the latter becomes more or less unconscious in us. The vital energy possibilities have to wait in the unconscious until consciousness gives meaning to them with its mind, giving us emotional thoughts. This is what we experience as a result of delayed choice and delayed collapse.

Why is this important? The organ hypothalamus in the mid-brain controls the pituitary gland, which in turn controls all the body hormones. Both organs belong to this midbrain chakra we are speculating about. If we can awaken the self at this chakra, we may be able to control the negative emotional brain circuits to a larger extent. That would constitute an enormous optimization of brain function.

The Negative Emotional Brain Circuits are Universal Software

Over the millions of years of evolution, the brain takes over the functions of the first four chakras in the body giving us the negative emotional brain circuits. These circuits are said to be instinctual.

Are instincts genetic in origin? Following Sheldrake, I (Amit) have theorized elsewhere (read my book *Creative Evolution*), that instincts are the gifts of liturgical/morphogenetic fields so conditioned as to function in all the detailed steps via which the instincts work, details that compel us to look for an epigenetic inheritance theory (in the same spirit as

Lamarckism – evolution via inheritance of acquired characteristics) for their origin.

How did the instinctual conditioning take place? Conditioning requires conscious events of learning. This is where the new hypothesis, that there is a tangled hierarchy and self-identity in the midbrain chakra comes handy.

These conditioned liturgical/morphogenetic fields along with their universal meanings given by our ancestors' collective ("tribal") consciousness using the mind reside in our collective unconscious; in that way, they become the universal vital-mental software of the negative emotional brain circuits that neuroscientists call unconscious memory.

Finally, the pleasure circuits originate and operate in the same way as above. They will be discussed later in the chapter.

Undoubtedly, there are potentialities of feeling in the various chakras, but are there selves at the chakras to experience them? In other words, does consciousness collapse the possibilities of feelings at the body chakras as well as yoga psychologists claim?

Recently, neuroscientists have discovered the presence of a bundle of nerves, a sort of a "brain" at both the navel and the heart chakra; this means memory-making capacity. We have been noting that the heart chakra in the form of the suspension of the immune system has the ability to cognize love; add the capacity of making memory to the cognitive capacity, what do you get? A tangled hierarchy, right? And that means only one thing: there is a self of the heart. By the same argument, there must be a self of the navel as well.

The experiences of feeling at these two chakras make memories that constitute personal vital software at these chakras. This we can put to empirical test. If this model is correct, then every one of us has a specialized personal software that comes with the organs where there is scope for making memory. So, if a dying person's heart is freshly transplanted into another living person's body, can the new owner feel the old feelings of the original owner of the organ? Yes, they can. They do. This has been a subject of much research and the verdict is based on that.

All male-dominated cultures of the old identify a "self of the body" at the navel. For example, in Japan, they call it *hara* and suicide is called *hara-kiri*, killing yourself is synonymous with killing your *hara*. Most people in modern times don't develop sensitivity to feeling energy in the body, they don't believe in it; and thus, they miss the experience of pure feeling. When men in our culture acquire sensitivity to feelings in the body, they begin to feel their self at the navel. Adds to their narcissism, but I guess it still is a good trend.

Women of course usually have some awareness of the self of the heart; that's why they swear by it often to men's consternation.

The neocortical thinking self-identity obscures these selves in the body from our easy conscious awareness of them. But again, it is not a complete take-over. When we wake up to the experiences of pure feelings at the navel and the heart chakras in connection with archetypal experiences, and give meaning to them with the neocortical self, using the psycho-neuro-gastro-intestinal and psycho-neuro-immunological connections respectively, we make positive emotional brain circuits.

Why are the chakras important, why are the feelings in the body other than the neocortex important? The body is important if we want to rewire the brain with emotional intelligence in mind. Emotional intelligence requires balancing the negativity that the negative emotional brain circuits create. But we cannot do that with the brain alone; only with the awareness of and exploration of positive feelings at the chakras can we creatively develop positive emotional brain circuits. The Quantum Yoga intensive course that I (Valentina) have developed together with Amit addresses the goal of this exploration. It is the search for Wholeness.

We would like to make one comment in passing. The dictionary definition of cognition is arriving at perception and understanding via thought. Quantum science is compelling us to use the word more generally. Cognition is the capacity of knowing: we can know through the use any of our experiences.

More on the Chakras

Go back to the chakra by chakra discussion of feelings at the chakras in an earlier chapter. Does some of this talk above about the usual experience of feelings even at the lower two chakras jive with your own experience?

Why do many Americans watch so much sex and violence on TV? Americans today live a very head-centered life; vital energy is always up there in the head in the chakra we call the brow chakra at the service of the thinking self. It gets dry. Could it be that watching sex and violence helps to bring up the energy from the sex chakra and the root chakra and collapse it in the brain to liven things up although most people are virtually unconscious of these vital movements?

In other words, even in the business of entertainment, somebody is trying to exploit you and keep you in line with the negativity and the pleasure-oriented competitive culture. Does this knowledge make you curious about exploring these chakras for their higher potentialities?

Furthermore, as mentioned earlier, during our evolution because of survival necessity, the brain has taken over the base-level operations of the body chakras anyway and made them into efficient instinctive brain circuit operations. But this is not true of the higher potentialities at any of these chakras, especially at the third and fourth chakra. Exploring these potentialities is how you can gain control back on your emotions, eventually on your body.

When energy moves into the heart from the lower sex and navel chakras for collapse, from the sex chakra after sex and the navel chakra after a good meal, you feel like giving, you feel vulnerable to your own generosity. Many men suppress the energy in their heart chakra because they don't want to become vulnerable to their partners. ''Maybe she will want an expensive gift or something''. Rewiring the brain for emotional intelligence can help overcome the fear of vulnerability and discover love.

In the same vein, many women would rather stay with an active heart and remain needy than reclaim their selves at the navel chakra and take responsibility. Rewiring the brain for emotional intelligence would help with that too.

How do we reprogram the brain beyond rewiring to create even more positivity? We have to do it in conjunction with the navel and heart chakra activities with the help of those little brains that have been discovered in those two chakras. We will tell you that wonderful story in a sequel *The Awakening of Intelligence*.

Right now, we are only using the potentialities of the brow chakra partially – acquiring knowledge through rational and emotional thought. The potentiality of intuitive thought remains unfulfilled for most people. When this potentiality of intuitive thought is fully actualized, the chakra is said to have fully opened. Metaphorically this is called the opening of the third eye – the eye of intuition. If you are one of those few with third eye even partly open, you will notice slight feelings of warmth whenever your creative intuitional energies are high.

The spiritual literature speaks very highly of the potentialities of the crown chakra. When this chakra opens, one develops the ability to dis-identify with the body producing the out-of-the-body experience, a capacity now much documented in many people.

Let's talk about pleasure. We have this basic survival instinct that expresses itself as drives that we call hunger, thirst, and sexuality. As a human being, you always cater to your basic conditioning that includes these instinctual drives. So, when you consider a relationship with another person and the implicit question you ask is, "What is in it for me?" there is a role that these basic drives play, an important role. If this person helps you satisfy any of these basic drives, your unconscious conclusion is "This person pleases me" or "I like this person." The opposite leads to the conclusion of dislike.

This implicit psychology of the human mind is true also about your relationship with things and phenomena. In this way, your "me" or ego always separates things into two categories: likes and dislikes.

The people you interact with notice your likes and dislikes in you and also in themselves. You (and everybody else) can be manipulated by using your likes and dislikes; it is like pushing a button. Except now we call them rewards and punishments. You please me; I will give you a reward, a pleasure. You oppose me; I will punish you by withholding the pleasure or even worse by subjecting you to the things you dislike.

Of course, the brain gets into this act pretty early on the evolution of mammals. So, we can find out how pleasure works in our brain by studying rats. In the nineteen sixties, the neuroscientists James Olds and Peter Milner pioneered the research on pleasure centers in the brain and they studied rats. These scientists intended to look for areas in the rat brain that when stimulated, would inhibit the rat from doing what it was doing, from doing its given task. But as they explored various areas of rat brain, they found areas which did the opposite. When they stimulated those areas, the rats could not stop doing what they were doing, they kept repeating the task.

Then these researchers changed the protocol. They allowed the rats themselves to stimulate the electrodes now implanted in those "pleasure areas." And guess what? The rats became so obsessed with pleasure that they would even ignore food and please themselves thousands of time and still not be satiated.

So which brain areas are we talking about? The perception area of course; additionally, the pleasure areas which respond to perception. The later area is called the ventral tegmental area (it is easier to remember the abbreviation VTA) located in the mid-brain.

Now you have to understand something basic about pleasure and in general about emotions. Feelings also have a physiological effect aside from mind giving meaning to them. You know this. How do you know that somebody is angry? You see his eyes and cheeks becoming red because of increased blood flow. That's how. In fact, much of cognitive-behavioral empathy training consists of learning how to interpret people's body language when they emote in various forms.

How does the person involved experience the physiological effect? The pronounced effect occurs when a neurotransmitter is emitted and fits into a receptor. In the case of pleasure, the neurotransmitter molecule is dopamine. The cells that produce the dopamine in the VTA feed two other important areas of the pleasure circuit: the nucleus accumbens and parts of the prefrontal cortex. The part in the prefrontal cortex is the reward circuit.

Two more important things: Firstly, many neuroscientists are confused that in the physiological effect, the molecule is the source of emotions including the feeling involved. Of course, nobody can deny that the effect of the molecule is spectacular. But we don't feel them, we sense them. And then our vital body gives feeling and mind gives meaning to the sensation and feeling in terms of the same like and dislike and things get further complicated. Undeniably though, the explosive component of pleasure comes from sensation; pleasure is sensual.

There is a second issue. The reward system based on pleasure has a side effect, another emotion. The emotion of desire, we *want* the objects of pleasure, we are driven to find them. So, is the circuit that Olds and Milner discovered a genuine pleasure/reward circuit or is it a pleasure/want circuit? Lots of new research is suggesting that both drives exist and the two drives use slightly different portions of the same pleasure circuit. The desire/want part of the circuit has its origin in the amygdala; desiring a pleasure-object is a prime negative emotion.

Rats and monkeys cannot handle pleasures; they drive themselves to death when pursuing pleasure. But fortunately, human beings have a brain that does satiate. Neuroscientists have discovered that part of the frontal cortex (called orbitofrontal cortex) is activated when subjects report sensations of the pleasure derived from drinking hot chocolate. But if the subjects drink too much chocolate, the brain areas do not show up activated in fMRI scanning.

It is a good thing too. I (Valentina) love chocolate. I don't know about dying for eating or drinking too much chocolate, but I would certainly get fat. So, I thank the brain for evolving this satiation aspect of the human pleasure circuit. But you know this is not the end of the story either. Don't forget the mind; mind gives meaning to the sensory experience, and that meaning says "want," "want," even when the brain does not cooperate. This takes us to the subject of addiction.

The story of pleasure is complicated. It starts with feelings having to do with perfectly essential biological functions. Then the mind gets into the act, gives meaning, producing some mischief. The emotions when satisfied also affect physiology, eventually ending up with molecules that generate powerful sensations. And mind gets into the act again giving meaning of "like-dislike" to the sensations/feelings and making more mischief.

The lesson is this. The human condition that the inertia in us, called *tamas* in Sanskrit, wants to perpetuate is unstable. If we try to be efficient and suppress pleasure-seeking emotions, we create stress. If we get into too much pleasure to please our "me"-centeredness, we get into addictions. Moderation is what we need and it is hard to practice.

Creativity research shows that in the early stages of creativity, situational creativity, we need the lure of rewards both during and after to motivate us: name, fame, money. Only when we become a little more intelligent, do we connect to the quantum self for motivation, the experience called inspiration. This gives us enthusiasm – the ability to engage creativity without looking for external reward later. But even so, connoisseurs have noticed that rewards help; a modicum of pleasure is good even for the soul.

Addiction messes up our pleasure and desire circuits, the associated memories and all related circuitry. Addiction is a chronic pathological condition with cycles of remission and relapse. Without treatment and rehab, addiction can be deadly. Addiction could be substance addiction; it also could be psychological. In either case, we cannot control our desires; we become helpless in our pursuit of relief.

We have already spoken of dopamine, the important neurochemical involved in the game of pleasure. How do drugs of addiction, such as cocaine and the like, hook a person? The dopamine hit one gets from a drug, especially in the beginning is stupendous, some two to ten times higher than normal sex or food can give. Yes, a pornographic image and even chocolate can give a ten times more intense dopamine high than normal. Imagine two to ten times higher amount of dopamine than what you are used to in normal pleasure activities floating around in the brain areas such as the nucleus accumbens! Neuroscientists say that this is what causes the euphoria, that ecstasy – I-am-the-king-of-the-world feeling – that is intoxicating, to say the least. Interesting enough, I (Valentina) have noticed that there is even a real addiction to pain and sufferance, aka masochistic tendencies, especially in children who grow up in disfunctional families. Dr. Gabor Mate has made a great contribution in ou understanding o this phenomenon.

All the drugs of addiction that you hear about – heroine, nicotine – produce dopamine high, but in somewhat different ways. In the case of heroin, they bind to the brain's opioid receptors in an area like the VTA, and that stimulates the release of high amounts of dopamine. Nicotine uses an intermediate, the acetylcholine receptor to stimulate dopamine production. That is what the pleasure of a puff of cigarette smoking is, sensing a dopamine molecule, feeling it, and mentally liking the feeling – a high.

Why do you get different highs with different drugs? Because each drug releases dopamine in its own way involving a different region of the brain in the pleasure area producing slightly different feelings, to which mind gives slightly different meanings, that's how. Also, the level of ecstasy that you reach is different for each drug, and the ego compares that.

If your aim of life is pleasure – eat, drink, and be merry (sex) – then drugs seem to be the logical next step. What's wrong with enhancing pleasure? Why can't it be a replacement for enhancing happiness as this book promises? If the reason we manifest consciousness is happiness, and who can deny pleasure is similar to happiness, only more intense (and you could say, therefore better!).

But there is a catch. What happens after you get hooked or addicted is disastrous. After the initial acquisition phase, there is a second phase of escalation. Why do people escalate their drug intake? Because they want to recapture the intensity of the first high, and that requires more and more of the drug. Also, the brain gives up its natural production; the brain also gets less and less sensitive to dopamine, all these factors contribute.

You need to understand the behavior of your brain in reaction to a drug that produces dopamine. Dopamine is a neurotransmitter that the brain neuron uses to communicate with other neurons to pass on its own activation to its neighbors. What extra dopamine due to a drug like alcohol does is to over-stimulate the neurons. When you take the drug again, the same amount does not produce as much high as the first time, so you think you are developing a tolerance, your body is getting used to the drug, and so you can take more; you can handle it. It's the opposite. Your brain is not getting used to the drug; it's shutting off some of the pathways to the adjacent neurons to protect them from dying. So, you increase the dosage, and to protect itself, the brain reduces more of its neuronal connections, and it takes you more alcohol to get the high. If you continue the process of indulging more, the brain continues its "down regulation" of removing even more neuronal connections. In truth, in spite of the brain's efforts, your brain neurons increasingly die as you imbibe more and more alcohol.

When I (Amit) was a graduate student, I remember being fascinated when a visiting Polish physicist took me out on a drinking spree and defined for me who a tough guy is. When I complained that I had enough, he said that in Poland, one has enough only when he feels compelled to go under the table and the hero – the tough guy – is the one who can drink until all his drinking buddies are under the table.

In reality the tough guy is getting serious brain damage. What stupidity is built into all human cultures all over the world to glamorise drug intake. Resorting to drugs for pleasure is anything but rational.

And this is only the second stage. What happens next is craving. This third stage is crucial and it is very important to understand it also. We begin with a liking of pleasure, pleasure of sensations that the pleasure molecules produce. At the third stage, the focus shifts to desire, craving.

You have to remember, every time we have a conscious experience, we make memory. We make memories of the feelings and sensing involved along with the meaning that we put on them; these memories make new software involving the reward areas. Of course, the amygdala gets involved since instinctual emotions come into play, too. And so does the hippocampus, since we are making conscious memory. This software constitutes the craving function. When we crave and develop withdrawal symptoms if we abstain, we have a serious addiction problem.

Why is all this important to know, that the new science is telling us? We cannot prune the neuronal circuits we create through drug addiction without producing serious damage, but we can change the mental and vital software through psychotherapy. Not ordinary psychotherapy mind you, but creative psychotherapy and quantum healing.

Food addiction is mainly sugar addiction, but it works in pretty much the same way as drug addiction via activation and modification of the pleasure circuitry of the brain. Perhaps food is not as strong an addictive as alcohol, heroine or nicotine, but its physical effect on the gastro-intestinal systems of the body as well as weight gain can be as harmful as the effect of nicotine on the throat chakra organs.

Some researchers suspect that there is also a genetic aspect in all this; drug addiction may be triggered by a genetic predisposition in some people.

Healing from Drug addiction

A person who has chosen to stay in the human condition come what may, is not going to engage creativity. Is there any other way to keep drug addiction under control or even heal drug addiction?

One reason we develop pleasure addiction is that human societies and religions try to coerce us into discipline against pleasure-seeking, and you know what? It is against human nature; we do not like coercion; I do not accept discipline that you want to impose upon me even though it would be for my own good and I know it. We want to retain our free will to learn through exploration.

Since curbing freedom just does not work, is there an alternative? Yes, of course. It is persuasion. Education and then persuasion through exemplifying is another way of educating people and open their door to being happy. Religious worldview is good in the first but falls short in the second. Religious teachers teach morality and ethics but do not exemplify. Material monism suffers from the same shortcoming. You cannot preach naturalness of pleasure-centeredness and then expect people to voluntarily not explore different avenues of pleasure or cut down on pleasure. Also, material monism pushes information processing over meaning processing; the young victims develop ADHD, and this has been found to lead to addiction.

The message is clear. If seeking pleasure and avoiding pain were the ways to live, food addiction, alcohol addiction, and other recreational drug addiction would have to be accepted as a natural progression of life for some people. But pleasure seeking dominates us only if we accept our base level human condition; only if we buy into material monism. Is there is more to life than are postulated in that philosophy?

The quantum worldview, in complete agreement with the spiritual traditions, says yes. There are infinite potentialities for us to explore. The purpose of life is the fulfillment of the potentialities for happiness: exploring meaning, feeling, the archetypes, and finally consciousness itself.

We got to go beyond our conditioned tendency of staying in the same place and oscillating between pleasure and pain. But you cannot teach people how to change staying within the human condition of inertia, the reason religious societies of the past failed and now material monism is failing coming from the opposite angle. Both worldviews impose contraction of consciousness; people need expansion of consciousness.

Quantum education emphacizes the seven I's: Inspiration, Intention, Intuition, Imagination, Incubation, Insight, and Implementation. Our intuitions are bringing us the winds of change every day. We have to teach addicts to be sensitive to these messages of expansion, and then follow through with quantum healing.

A complete discussion of quantum healing of addiction is beyond the scope of this book. Read our upcoming book *Quantum Integrative Medicine*.

Questions to Ponder Upon

1. Ponder over the chakras and the brain's relationship with the chakras in the body.
2. Are you convinced that chakras are real? Can you experience feelings in your navel and heart chakra? Meditate on them with powerful visualizations given in many available books of chakra psychology.
3. Have you experienced animal consciousness? Ponder over it. Are you convinced that there has to be a chakra at the mid-brain?
4. Drugs and addiction are wrong ways to change the brain; the inorganic ones alter the brain by suppressing gene expression but do not give the brain

any new software or function; they mostly keep us away from expansion of consciousness. Organic plants used by spiritual traditions may introduce new vital software in the brain and cause new experiences; so, they could be an exception. Think about this.

5. Have you had any personal experience with drugs and addiction? Do you think the exposition here may help addicts?

6. Finally, consider. Neuroscientists have been telling us about unconscious brain actions and unconscious memory for the last fifty years making it seem completely hopeless to try to change the brain's behavior. The most important message of this book is this: all the software in the brain, universal and personal, were and are created by conscious choice and collapse. Be empowered. What we create, we can undo, in the least we can optimize the situation.

CHAPTER 5

Mind, Meaning, and Memory

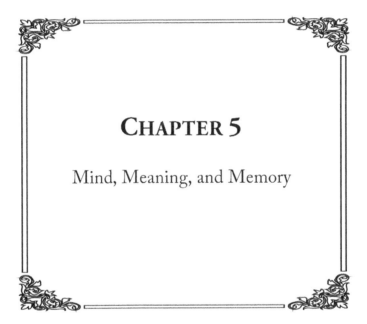

As consciousness recognizes and collapses a particular state from the quantum possibilities of the brain (mind) in response to a stimulus, it not only collapses the brain memory of the neuronal circuit but also the correlated mental meaning. In the process of perception, consciousness uses the brain to make representations of the physical world but it is the mental meanings of the representations that we see. When subsequently, the same stimulus arrives at the brain, it is the correlated mental memory that plays out, the brain memory that is evoked in response to a stimulus just acts as a trigger for the mental memory.

There is advantage that memory works this way in the brain compared to the computer. In a computer, we recall memory by simply pushing a button. But ask yourself: where is the button to push for a brain? Sure, a neurosurgeon can cut up the skull and poke suitable areas of the brain, and there comes memory! But we do not, cannot do it that way, do we?

We seem to do it by intention; it requires consciousness. Hence, neuroscientists make models to avoid any role of consciousness. One such model is called the library model. Your intention is a command to the CPU of your brain's computer that then calls up the memory classified by some sort of numbering system like books in a library. But that model is of limited validity since much of our memory involves different regions of the brain. In a second model, the analogy consists of a crime scene investigation where the brain's CPU plays the role of the detective in charge to put the clues together.

Both models get bogged down when you ask, where does my intention come from? Where do I come from? In quantum neuroscience, these questions are answered from the get-go. Brain memory and its associated mental meaning are both quantum possibilities in our unconscious. When we intend, unconscious cooperates and collapses the appropriate memory. This is a law of quantum neuroscience. Of course, the collaboration of our unconscious depends on certain factors such as attention and interest (how much feeling and meaning you bring to the occasion), the history of past recalls (probability of recall is enhanced by recall). That, too, is part of the dynamics.

The quantum way of looking at memory recall also agrees very well with the experimental findings of neurosurgeon Wilder Penfield. Penfield conducted extensive research with epileptic patients, and probed their brains with electrodes in search of the so-called memory "engram." He did find little groups of neurons which, when activated by poking with electrodes played out entire symphonies! How can a little piece of the brain contain so much memory?

And in his entire search, Penfield never found an area which when poked, anything like CPU/self would be experienced by his subject. Thus, Penfield concluded that there must be a non-physical consciousness. Yes, it is consciousness that uses the brain for mental memory making and it is consciousness that is retrieving it. Of course, in those early days, Penfield thought dualistically. In this quantum age, all of us can think with monistic idealism, non-dual consciousness, quantum self, and ego, whichever you want.

Some memories are already built in the brain; your brain comes with them such as the instincts and the negative emotional brain circuits. That memory is called implicit or unconscious. In the quantum model, the unconscious here is the collective unconscious, beyond your ego-control. It is the memory that you make consciously, i.e., the conscious or explicit memory that is at issue here. Part of the explicit memory is called declarative memory. Why this name? You can declare something about it: "It was raining and it was making me feel sad" is a statement of declarative memory. Another name, episodic memory, is used for conscious memory that is autobiographical: "You want to know how my wife and I met? It is a long story." When you tell that story, that story is coming from episodic memory.

Neuroscientists say there are four steps of declarative memory: acquisition, storage, retrieval, and forgetting. Before new memory is made, you must acquire new information to memorize. This is the acquisition phase. Then the memory must be stored somewhere. This will enable you to hold the memory in place until you need to retrieve it. This constitutes the storage phase. Retrieval is remembering. Forgetfulness is not difficult to understand: memory that you cannot retrieve any more by simply intending, even intending with associations, you have forgotten.

Storage is something neuroscientist study by monitoring amnesia victims as a result of specific parts of the brain being surgically removed. For example, if the hippocampus is removed, the victim will have a major case of amnesia, giving neuroscientists valuable information that the hippocampus is a major player in memory making. This is the "where" aspect of the story of storage.

There is also a "when" aspect of memory. This is even more interesting for you to know. Memory goes through some distinct period before it becomes permanent.

It is the other two steps – acquisition and retrieval – that challenge the materialist approach to neuroscience to no end. Above, we have solved the retrieval problem readily, using the quantum model of memory recall. What can we say about acquisition with quantum neuroscience to sort out knots in the existing model?

Memory Acquisition

Maybe you already know what a neuron looks like and how it works. If you don't, we are giving you the bare bone of what is essential to know in order to understand the problem we are facing.

Look at fig. 11 a. The neuron has a cell body, a long fiber called axon that caries electrical information along its length ending up at a junction called the synapse. Then there are the little fibers called dendrites all along the axon; those connect to other neurons.

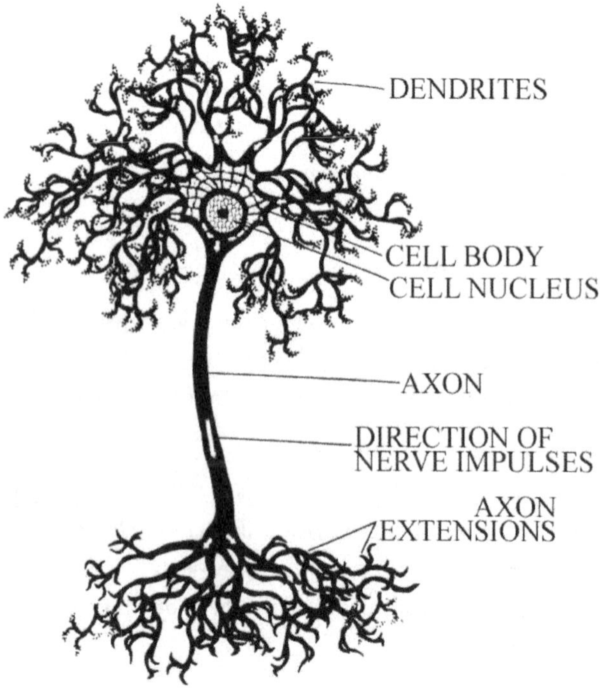

Figure 11 a. The neuron

The neuron works in four stages:

1. Neurotransmitter molecules (such as glutamate and dopamine) from other neurons stimulate dendrites of the neuron; the pulses so created move along the dendrite to the neuron's main cell body.

2. The cell body combines all the hundreds of dendritic pulses it receives, some positive or excitatory, some negative or inhibitory. The inhibitory pulses are necessary to prevent epilepsy-like situation (when brain becomes ablaze with neurons firing all over) and give stability.

3. If the net, positive plus negative, passes a threshold, a voltage pulse (an all or nothing electrical response) is created. The neuron fires, in other words. This pulse travels down the body of the long axon to the presynaptic terminal of the synapse.
4. At the fourth and final stage, the electrical pulse triggers a chemical pulse of neurotransmitter molecules that are released into the synaptic cleft. These molecules quickly diffuse to the postsynaptic receptor sites of the membrane of the dendrites of the post-synapti`c neuron (fig. 11b). The receptor site acts as the lock to the neurotransmitter molecule's key.

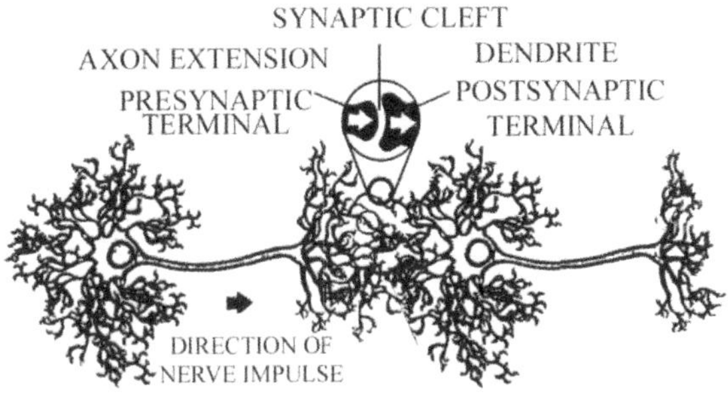

Figure 11 b. How neurons communicate and form networks that we call *brain circuits*

Now, let's get to the basic concept of memory-making as a neuronal brain circuit. Ordinarily, according to our scenario above, a neuron has a fifty-fifty chance to fire: it may, it may not. When we say your consciousness makes a new memory of a recognizable meaningful event of perception in a brain circuit, this fifty-fifty situation changes. Now the group of neurons making up the brain circuit has achieved a situation where the firing efficiency of the group as a whole is much bigger, say ninety percent, than the average fifty. If the circuit fires, the brain circuit has made a new memory of the correlated mental meaning. This memory will henceforth be evoked in your conscious awareness upon receiving the stimulus or simply by your willingness to recall it.

This that is how Penfield's data, memory in a localized engram, is explained. Is this true of declarative memory of simple facts and events in general? No, it is not always so simple, the structure of the neuronal circuit.

The biologist author John Medina compares memory making with the working of a blender running with its lid off. In other words, a simple fact may be sliced and diced, and grated, before finding its appropriate neuronal site. Explains Medina:

One woman suffered a stroke in a specific region of her brain and lost the ability to use written vowels. You could ask her to write down a simple sentence, such your dog chased the cat" and it would look like this:

Y_ _r d_g ch_s_d th_ c_t

(Medina, Brain Rules, pg 105)

She would leave the vowel spaces blank. Vowels and consonants are stored in different places in the brain; the part of her brain that memorizes the vowel space is no longer accessible.

How does your consciousness bind together information in two distant places in the brain and still give you the unity of experience? This is a puzzle for the conventional approach: the previously mentioned binding problem.

But, is this a puzzle for the quantum model of memory? No. Through its non-local capacity, consciousness can correlate neurons of as many sites as necessary for processing to make a neuronal circuit of memory. And this is something that the brain cannot do with only local material interactions. People always credit neuroscientist Donald Hebb as the theorist who explained memory, but Hebb's local theory is not the complete story. Hebb was also missing the mind part of memory. This quantum model of the non-local brain circuit with correlated mental meaning explains all things about memory.

Temporal Storage

There are other aspects of memory that are also puzzling for the materialist approach. We all experience, and neurophysiologists have found much data corroborating our experience, that there are three kinds of memory: working memory, short term memory, and long-term memory. Why three kinds?

The answer comes with the acknowledgement of the role of the mind in memory as above. On closer scrutiny, we find that working memory is memory we work with in the present moment; it requires a rather small memory space. This is handy for stuff with only temporary significance – a phone number for example that we are dialing but will not need in the future, we let go of it after our job is finished. Working memory that works with significant thoughts that we may need later we try not to let go. We recall them over and over and this makes them into short-term memory.

Why two types – short-term memory and long-term memory for such meaningful stuff that we don't want to let go? Why not just one kind?

We have the capacity to recall memory, of being conscious that we have been conscious before. And we use these recalls to reinforce the memory, but the nature of recall goes through half a second of secondary processing that edits and reconstructs them sometimes with the help and influence of other memories that are evoked by the stimulus. In other words, short-term memory is *reconstructive memory*. That is how we build a self-image and persona. Using short term reconstructive memory that can be inauthentic!

Only after a while, we settle down on a particular piece of memory when it is in equilibrium with our self-image and that is when it becomes stored as "permanent" long-term memory, a process called consolidation. This is the memory that even Alzheimer patients retain until late stages!

It is estimated that it takes roughly up to ten years of processing at the short-term scale before the memory becomes long-term ones. In the meantime, what we recall is not "fact"; they are reconstructive and are constantly in flux for a period. You should always remember this in connection with relationships.

Why Distinguish between Working Memory and Short-term Memory?

It behooves us to go over why it is necessary to make a distinction between working and short-term memory. Conventional cognitive neuroscientists do not make this distinction.

Consider an experiment the neuroscientist typically does to study the nature of working memory. They will give a bunch of subjects a string of words to listen to at a rate of about one word per second. The string is usually 30 words long, such as quantum, fruit, cognition, element, table, moon, and so forth, unrelated words. Immediately, following the listening to the last word, the participants are asked to recall back as many words as they can in any order they prefer. Guess what? People usually cannot recall more than 12, at most 15 words. This is reason that there is a limit on how long a telephone number can be.

But here is a mild surprise. People usually will remember the first few words (primacy effect) and the last few words (recency effect), but nothing in between.

God is in the details. As an explanation, the cognitive neuroscientist will tell you this. At any given moment, the storage place for working memory is capable of holding only five or six words. So, as you listen progressively to a string, the space will be continually erased and replaced by new words. Got it?

Why the recency effect? As a subject listens to a word, the latter goes into the working memory until the storage is filled up. When the next word comes, it must bump a previous word out of the memory, and so forth until the last five or six words at the end for which there is no need to bump any more. It's easy and mechanical. A Newtonian machine can do it!

But to explain the primacy effect, listen to the description that the neuroscientist gives. Let's say, you are listening. As you listen to the first word quantum, you will try to memorize it by quickly regurgitating it a few times (quantum, quantum, quantum…) and you will succeed, no doubt. So, the first word will become part of the recallable memory. As the second word of the string, fruit, comes, your attention will be divided between the two words; but still fifty percent attention is not bad, and you easily will succeed in making this word also quite recallable. So, on it goes until about the sixth word. When the seventh word arrives, your attention to it is much reduced; in this way, the probability of recalling it will be low. Thus, only the first few words are privileged to go into recallable memory.

But this process requires attention. What is attention based on, have you noticed? It is based on meaning, cognition. And this is where the establishment cognitive neuroscientist is making an unjustifiable assumption that the brain can cognize which it can't.

So here is then the difference. Making working memory is purely mechanical while making recallable memory is anything but mechanical; it requires your consciousness and mind, meaning-giving capacity. Therefore, although no new storage space is involved, we must call it by a new name – short term memory.

Awareness, Attention, Interest, and Memory

When we are awake and generally taking on the scene around us, initially, there is arousal of awareness, an external field generated by our senses dominated by vision of course, and an internal field dominated by thought. As we said before, what we perceive externally is generated after we have given it some sort of meaning (for animals they see what they see through feeling); this is a kind of universal meaning, a part of our collective unconscious. (Similarly, the general feelings associated with physical objects are part of the universal liturgical software.)

Suddenly something, some material object catches our focus and we call that attention. It works the same way for our internal sky. Thoughts arrive, one after the other. And suddenly one thought catches our attention again.

So, what does grab our attention? Things that are of interest to us in terms of either meaning or both feeling and meaning, that is, emotion. When an object grabs our specific attention, we may associate further personal meaning or emotion to it. And this personalization of the experience with specific meanings and emotions is very important for memory recall, recall of conscious or declarative memory.

There is cognitive evidence that understanding helps in recalling memories. The cognitivists Bransford and Johnson did an experiment with two groups; the groups were to read a passage and memorize it and were to be tested later. One group was given the contextual meaning of the passage but not the other group. Here is the passage:

The procedure is actually quite simple. First you arrange items in different groups. Of course, one pile may be sufficient depending on how much there is to do. If you have to go somewhere else due to lack of facilities, that is the next step; otherwise you are pretty well set. It is important not to overdo things. That is, it is better to do few things at once than too many. In the short run, this may not seem important, but complications can easily arise. A mistake can be expensive as well. At first, the whole procedure will seem complicated. Soon however, it will just become another facet of life. It is difficult to foresee any end to the necessity of this task in the immediate future, but then, one never can tell. After the procedure is completed one arranges the materials into different groups again. Then they can be put in their appropriate places. Eventually they be used once more and the whole cycle will then have to be repeated. However, that is part of life.

When I (Amit) myself read this passage without the meaningful context, it did not make much sense and I could not recall much either. I suspect it will be the same with you as it was for the experimental group who did not know. The group that was told the contextual meaning,-by the way, it was doing the laundry, the memorization and retrieval was no problem.

There is another aspect of all this, I hope you see it and rebel. Our conditioned minds, with its mental meanings soft-wired into the brain, permits us to process only a small portion of all the stimuli it receives, and as stated above, generally speaking, this is good. However, who is being the boss here, you or your brain? In this fashion, paying attention to attention and awareness and increasing your interest about your environment is also your way to get back some control about who decides what gets into your conscious awareness.

The lesson to learn from the involvement of the mind in the storage of memory is very important for parents, educators, and child psychologists. Mind is for processing meaning. If you want to retrieve something easily, it better be meaningful to you over a time.

Today's materialist culture emphasizes on processing information, not meaning. Information will be available on the internet, kids are told. All you have to know is how to retrieve it. The flaw in this argument is manifold. One is simply that information is other people's meaning. What you retrieve from the internet is other people's meaning, not yours. A second problem is information is much harder to remember than when you derive the meaning of it yourself. So, what happens with this information-based approach is that a kid can learn a subject enough to ace an exam, but then he or she rapidly forgets the information. You have to remember a little even to use the internet effectively. Thus, learning is impaired. Since rational thinking depends on the accumulated ability to retrieve memory, eventually the ability of rational thinking itself is compromised. This is how informationally dumbed down people cannot distinguish between the nonrational and irrational when they become (justifiably) rebels against excessive use of rationalism, and become easy victims of conspiracy theories.

Today, it is common for many children to develop the attention deficit hyperactive disorder (ADHD). The attention deficit has also to do with the de-emphasis on meaning that is prevalent in our culture. I (Valentina) have noticed too many such cases in young adults as well, nowadays; some of them are even teaching others psychology related stuff or even healing (in a continuously anxious state).

Lack of attention is serious business. When we attend, we are putting our choice in line and movement of consciousness goes along with our choice. However, when we do not actively attend but are only passively aware, behaviors are collapsed according to our habit patterns on a statistical basis, and not necessarily in tune with the current moment and necessity. This is how entropy is created in the processing of the mind and one of its symptoms is ADHD.

Emotional Memory

Usually declarative memory takes maybe seven or eight repetitions before it is permanent enough to be delegated to the status of short-term memory. But, you know, if the event is loaded with emotions, then it may take only one repetition to remember forever. (Of course, it would still be reconstructed repeatedly before becoming long-term.)

While writing this chapter, a scene from the past came back to me (Amit) so vividly that I was overwhelmed with the emotion of nostalgia. I was fiftyish then and married to my second wife. We had stayed up all night playing a card game of spades with friends, another biracial couple like ourselves. In the aftermath, my male friend was shaving, the two women were making breakfast, and I was just watching, taking in the scene with love.

You know, I have not consciously thought of this event in ages, if ever. And yet, such is the power of emotion on memory.

So, the lesson is this. If you give emotional meaning to what you research, if you engage with feelings and emotions with things you experience, the memory of those things will be so much easier to recall. People often ask me on occasions they take my workshops when I present lectures for 20-30 hours without consulting any notes or books, "How do you remember so much?" Mainly this is because I mostly talk about my personal discoveries all of which were the results of passion. Some of other people's work that I present, such as basic quantum physics, I remember because I have given these concepts meaning and there was passion in the processing of that meaning too.

You may ask, what's the difference when you remember this way versus as information processing, writing down in a PowerPoint presentation? In fact, a PowerPoint with thoughtfully written words may be even easier to understand for workshop participants! Well, it is not like that. When your memory is easy-without-effort, your ego can play creatively with the quantum self while the presentation is going on – a play psychologists call ''flow''. Everyone in the audience including the presenter can feel the presence of the quantum self and creativity, it is so inspiring. That is the difference.

Protecting Your Child from Future Dementia

There is now a theory of Alzheimer disease that is gaining traction: Alzheimer's disease is an autoimmune disease. Valentina and I did extensive research on this subject, since we saw that more and more people can manifest it, even at young age. You will be able to read more in our upcoming book on medicine. The point is that in Alzheimer's disease, the immune system malfunctions and starts attacking its own body's cells; that is the general idea. But one suspects that Alzheimer's disease might happen to people even when their immune system is okay.

The alternative is that some cells may become unrecognizable to the immune system as belonging to the body in which case it will attack. What is it that makes brain cells unrecognizable to the immune system? Quantum science gives us a hint. The purpose of a neuron in the neocortex is to help consciousness process meaning (in all people) and purpose (for some woke people). People who habitually process only information and never any meaning or purpose, they are in the danger of effectively losing their "identity card" with their immune system.

In case the last comment requires explanation, ask yourself, "How does the immune system identify a cell in the body as a cell belonging to 'me?'" Early on, for every cell in the body, the immune system leaves a marker, an identity card so to speak. This is similar to how the antibody works in response to any bacterial or virus attack that you hear about.

In the famous nun study, there is suggestive evidence of a strong association between early-adult linguistic abilities and dementia at old age. Researchers studied the handwritten autobiographical manuscripts of apprentice nuns in their first year at a convent – nuns of average age of 23. Sixty years later, these nuns were studied as to their mental acuity. Moreover, after-death autopsy was done on them with permission. Nuns whose autobiographical notes were relatively ho-hum in meaningful ideas and linguistic flare were the ones who were found likely to get Alzheimer at old age.

Parents, be aware!

Questions to Ponder Upon

1. Compare the theory of memory developed here with your own experience.
2. Do you agree with the idea of reconstructive memory – that memory changes over time, or we reconstruct them so to speak? Do you find it difficult to

acknowledge that your recall of an episodic memory of common experience may not be entirely right when somebody else claims so?

3. Ponder on the distinction between attention, awareness, and mindfulness.
4. Ponder on the importance of such factors as interest, emotions, value needs on making memories.
5. Think about the distinction of working memory and short-term memory proposed here. Does it make sense?
6. Many old people suffer from brain dementia of memory recall – Alzheimer's disease. While reading this chapter, ponder about some remedies that can help against such diseases.

CHAPTER 6

How the Self Acquires I—I/me Polarity: Brain Evidence

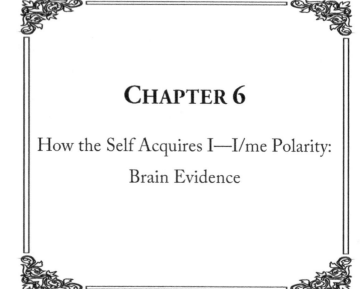

The everyday consciousness that we normally experience is not the tangled hierarchical numinous quantum self, but the simple hierarchical conditioned phenomenon that we call the ego. Ego's nature is to maintain a status quo, a control over its fixed programs. Thus, the ego can become a barrier to our exploration of the quantum self.

How does this ego arise if our initial subject-response to every external stimulus/object should be the quantum self? Every time the apparatus of the tangled hierarchy processes a stimulus, it makes a memory of the stimulus-response. What does the response consist of? A subject that I can look at as "me", and the object; this goes into memory. Next time the same stimulus arrives at the brain, the memory plays back giving a secondary stimulus, a reflected image so to speak. So, the brain's perception system has to respond not only to the primary stimulus but also to the secondary stimulus. With more and more reflection in the mirror of such memory, I-object experience of the quantum self is more and more replaced by a memory experience, me-object. What repeated reflection in the mirror of memory does is 1) bias the system to respond in favor of the previous response. This way, several such reflections produce what psychologists call conditioning. And 2) the conditioned subject that we eventually experience has little subject/I and more the objectified "I" that we call "me". On the average, the me-experiences dominate the I-experiences. Thus, the quantum self becomes implicit in our everyday ego experience, a state of the subject we call I/me.

Repeatedly learning to respond to stimuli with stimulus-response-reinforcement mechanisms as above produces 1) an entire pattern of conditioned mental and/or emotional habits and 2) a repertoire of learned traits of a human self that we call our ego's character.

What's the difference between a mere habit and a learned trait, an ability that you have cultivated, that comes to your aid whenever you intend? A habit is a tendency, never absolutely conditioned; this is why you can change it. A learned character trait is an ability, for example riding a bicycle. You never lose the ability. Habit is acquired via continuous change. You acquire a character trait via a discontinuous change, a *quantum leap*.

In Newtonian worldview, all movement is continuous. In the quantum worldview, movement can be continuous as well which is familiar to you, right? Movement of both thought and feeling seems continuous in your everyday experience that we call stream of consciousness. But the physicist Niels Bohr discovered in 1913 that when electrons jump from one atomic orbit to another, they jump discontinuously, without going through the intermediate space. This is called a quantum leap.

A collapse of quantum possibility into actuality leading to the discovery or invention of something new is a discontinuous quantum leap. Only when we move from one conditioned experience to another, does the quantum discontinuity of the collapse give way to continuity.

Thus, quantum theorizing is giving us an explanation of the behavioral ego that is more inclusive than cognitive/neurophysiological models of conditioned neuronal pathways in neural networks in the brain causing behavior. The latter can explain only conditioned behavior. In the quantum model, there is always room for creative behavior which is about going beyond conditioned behavior altogether in response to internal novel stimuli that we call intuition. We need the two-self model – quantum self and ego/character built in the quantum way – to explain both conditioned and creative behaviors and the many shades in between.

Psychologists talk about the experience of flow most often in connection with creative enterprises and they are joyful. Yet you may have had such experiences while dancing or other physical activities like golfing or playing football. All athletes talk about being "in the zone." These are also undeniably examples of flow.

How does flow happen while doing a learned task? Practice, practice, and practice. Have you heard that story about a New York tourist and the music virtuoso? The tourist was lost so he asked the virtuoso who was passing by, "What is the way to the Carnegie Hall?" Carnegie hall is the famous Music Hall where only virtuosos get to perform. "Practice, practice, practice," responds the virtuoso of course. The tourist would be puzzled by the response but you would get a laugh.

But seriously, what practice does is produce mastery and you can relax while performing the task. As you relax, you fall into the quantum self. In this way flow is the result of our using both self-identities. Flow happens when we alternate effortlessly between the ego/character and the quantum self; the joy of flow comes from the encounter with the quantum self. Also, when we are in flow, we clearly experience dependent co-arising: that feeling that we are not doing it – it is just happening by itself.

The Ego/Character/Persona

However, the ego that we normally experience is not the ego/character but what psychologists correctly call ego/character/persona. The character is masked by programs of behavior that change from situation to situation. This ego/character/persona is simple hierarchical; the ego seems to choose the program of its behavior much like the CPU of a computer does; the tangled hierarchy is pretty much obscured. Moreover, some of the masks of the persona are authentic, more or less conforming to our character; but some of them are inauthentic, we wear the mask to hide our real character.

What converts an ego I/me with a bunch of habit patterns, character traits, and learned repertoire to a simple hierarchical doer? First of all, the conditioning accompanying any learning of a stimulus is not 100% for any specific response. In practice, we learn a series of responses to the same stimulus with a varying amount of weighted probabilities. For example, chocolate might be your favorite ice cream, but sometimes you do choose vanilla, or even banana, right? Second, memory making is a complex process, remember? For example, there are short-term and long-term memories. So, when we say reflection in the mirror of memory, which memory are we talking about? We are talking mostly about short-term reconstructive memory that can create inauthenticity. Third, we have the ability of being conscious (before); so, we can use this ability ad infinitum and in fact, we often do. In this way, I can look at the task and make myself into an appropriate "me" and act accordingly. The net effect is that we are choosing our behavior for a particular situation from a whole spectrum of personality programs, a bunch of masks that we identify with at different moments. This is our simple hierarchical ego/character/persona with the quantum self/real "I", virtually all hidden and a simple hierarchical "I/me" having taken its place that is more or less a "me." This is what we all refer to as "I" but mean just "me." And who can blame me for this illusory construction? The "I" that I experience is one that I can introspect and make into "me"; add to this the fact that I am deciding which behavior of my conditioned spectrum of behavior I will choose (for example I choose the flavor of ice cream I want, given a choice) and thirdly, I choose whatever mask I want to wear in a given situation.

A swan had landed near a well and met a frog jumping about in the well. Out jumped the frog and asked, "Who are you? Where are you going?"

"I am swan. I am going across the sea," The swan replied.

"How big is the sea?" the frog was curious.

"The sea is very, very big," said the swan.

The frog jumped a distance and asked, "That big?"

"Much, much bigger," said the swan. This time the frog jumped a few times, and asked the same question, "That big?"

The swan still shook his head, "Much bigger."

The fog got so rattled that it jumped its way all around the well and cried, "The sea cannot be any bigger, can it?"

The swan insisted, "The sea is vast."

The frog could not believe the swan. "The swan must be deluded," he concluded.

This is the worst part of the ego/persona contraction of our consciousness. We cannot believe in the expansion of consciousness and the freedom it brings any more.

Is there free will after all this covering of the real freedom and creativity available in the quantum self? There are experiments that show that whereas we can flex a finger within 200 milliseconds in response to an external signal, if we are asked to voluntarily flex our finger, it takes a second or more to do so from the time of onset of electrical activity connected with the action in the brain, which can be measured by an EEG machine. The response of the EEG (upon elimination of noise) is called the readiness potential. The explanation fits the notion that the response to an external signal is unconscious brain action, it is mechanical. It seems, even the thought of so-called free-willing at the ego-level does not surface without its processing time. And execution of the "free" willing thought takes even longer. Many neuroscientists thus believe that they have put the subject of free will to rest. There is no free will.

But wait! The neuroscientist Benjamin Libet asked subjects to flex one hand at the wrist while also noting the position of a spot on a revolving disk (like the second hand of a clock) as to when they formed their intention. A few seconds afterwards, the subjects told the experimenter where the spot was when a conscious will was made, which enabled Libet to calculate the time of that event. Libet found that there indeed was a time lag of around 400 milliseconds or so between the onset of the readiness potential and the awareness of the will to flex the wrist. This further supports the above idea. The ego seems to be simply not free to will anything.

However, Libet discovered a twist. Although the will to flex the wrist is formed before we become aware of that will in thought, we are able subsequently to stop our willed action during the 200 or so milliseconds that remains between the actual action and the thought. What is the explanation? Even in our ego identity, we are not totally conditioned (remember, a 100% conditioned response requires an infinite amount of conditioning). So, we are able to say "no" to conditioning. This is important to remember: to open the door for creativity is as simple as developing a knack for saying "no" to conditioning, no to the conditioned response, *neti*-in Sanskrit, not this, developing what we call an open mind.

Is there unconscious brain action that precedes any of our willed action though? Does the readiness potential prove at least that much when there is no external stimulus? Does this also imply that the brain *can* cognize an external situation and begin preparation before we think and act? No, we are not thinking the quantum way.

The experimental situation creates a whole bunch of possibilities in the brain-mind of the subject. When a subject has a verbal thought of free will, he not only collapses that possibility but also a whole bunch of possibilities of brain action that must causally precede his verbal thought (retroactively, see below). The experimenter's intention and measurement interfere and collapse the brain possibility of the subject at the outset, producing the readiness potential. Just as you can look at a sleeping person and collapse her sleeping body in your awareness, similarly, an experimenter can monitor her brain waves while she sleeps.

One final comment before we close shop here. What about those people who develop "faith," a belief so strong that they won't budge from it, no matter what? There indeed are people who would rather die for their belief, faith than quit on it. We call such people fundamentalists, but what produces this phenomenon if 100% conditioning takes infinite repetitions and is practically impossible? The answer is that these people reinforce their beliefs so much that they are able to relax in their belief. Then they fall into the quantum-self accompanied by a feeling in the gut or a feeling in the heart that we normally associate with an experience of the "truth." So, who can blame them from believing that that their belief is the only truth?

Freud introduced not only the concept of the unconscious but also another very enigmatic concept, enigmatic that is for the materialists, called preconscious. At first sight, this may even seem to be enigmatic from a quantum science point of view. Unconscious is potentiality unmanifest, conscious is manifest, the result of actualization of potentiality, that's easy to conceive. Freud is saying that in between these two states, we have a twilight zone called the preconscious. How can that be? Either there is collapse, or there isn't. How can there be a halfway situation? Let's consider a compelling example.

We have a persistence of vision that enables us to see a parade of still pictures at a rate of twenty-four frames a second as a motion picture – this is the so-called phi phenomenon. When we do the parade in colors, the so-called color phi, what happens will take you by surprise.

In the simplest arrangement, an experimenter illuminates in quick succession two spots separated by an angle of three or four degrees. Observers see this as a single spot moving back and forth. No surprise there. When one of the illumined spots is red and the other is green though, a red spot is seen first as expected, which then moves and changes color abruptly to green at the halfway point of its imaginary passage, henceforth it travels as green to the second location. Observers can even point to where the color switch took place with a pointer. And they see the effect even in their first trial – it is not a conditioned reflex or anything like that.

This phenomenon of color phi was first observed by cognitivists Paul Kolers and Michael von Grünau in 1976. The experimenters illuminated each spot for 150 milliseconds with a 50-milliseconds pause in between.

From the materialist point of view that there is a seat of consciousness in the brain, a CPU, there is something deeply disturbing about the color phi phenomenon. The puzzling question is this: how can one perceive green before green is lit?

The philosopher Daniel Dennett in his book *Consciousness Explained* has analyzed this phenomenon and he correctly says that there are two alternatives – both unpalatable nightmares – from the seat-of-consciousness (which he calls the Cartesian theater; not a bad name because the materialist view is actually a hidden dualism, consciousness is implicitly assumed) point of view. As mentioned earlier, there is a time delay before we see anything in consciousness and during this period some tricky preconscious editing takes place in the "editing room" of the Cartesian theater. For example, the first frame that arrives is, of course, the red spot. But when the green frame arrives, the editing room inserts fictitious frames, additional red and green frames, and it is this edited version that finally makes it to consciousness and that gives the impression of motion and the change of color midway through the movement. Dennett calls this the Stalin-esque scenario; again, very appropriately. You know, Stalin killed some 60 million people, but nobody suspected it at the time he did it. But when we found out about it later after he died what a nightmare it was!

Interestingly, if subjects are asked to press a button as soon as they "see" the red spot alone, versus a red followed by a green spot 200 milliseconds later, the response time can be less than 200 milliseconds! Thus, in the Stalin-esque scenario such button pushes, like the editing, must also be preconsciously edited.

In Dennett's second scenario, called the Orwellian scenario (dystopian nightmare – the twenty-first century phenomenon of Donald Trump and other aspiring dictators in previously democratic countries – predicted in 1984), the frame insertions take place as a post-conscious revision of memory/history of the events before the verbal report. Since the subject can only verbally report what is in his or her memory, obviously an Orwellian post-conscious revision of history is as much an explanation of the color phi phenomenon as the preconscious Stalin-esque scenario.

In the quantum explanation, the phenomenon has no puzzle at all; instead it gives data in support of what we call primary and secondary process events of preconscious modulation. What does preconscious mean? Exactly that. They are the primary quantum self-event and all the secondary processing collapses of some pure "I"-events mixed with mostly I/me events that precedes the actual event of collapse of the I/me that one actually experiences. These primary and secondary events preceding the actual collapse event all take place retroactively going backward in time. This way of collapsing events is called delayed choice. We call these events "imperience"; they are not experience in the usual sense but they indeed causally influence what we experience at the present moment of actualization. Because of all these preconscious imperiences there are red frames, then overlapping red and green frames and then green frames alone that are presented on the screen of our theater. Mind trying to make sense of the pattern creates the amazing illusion that we actually see—that the green light must have come on while the red was still on. In this way, the quantum view sides with the Stalin-esque rather the Orwellian scenario of Dennett, thus removing the ambiguity.

By the way, a spiritually enlightened mystic named Franklin Merrell-Wolff created this word "imperience" because mystics too have experiences which seem to be the aftermath of delayed choice. Read Amit's book, *See the World as a Five-layered Cake*.

Do these delayed choice events happen? Yes, they do; in principle they should be in our memory. Read on.

Delayed Choice

Sooner or later you are bound to catch onto a puzzle about our discussion earlier about the time lag between the quantum self-experience and the ego experience. The possibilities are not actualized until we in the ego experience subject-object split. When an event takes place at the ego level, how can we glibly talk about secondary and/or primary actualization events of imperience taking place before that when clearly the subject-object split awareness must take place only when ego I-me, as subject, am aware of the event at the present moment?

Don't puzzle any longer. In quantum physics, imperiences can happen because of what we call delayed choice. Yes, ego I/me's choice (which consciousness goes along with) and the actualization occurs later, the events of imperience that causally precedes this ego event wait in potentiality until the ego (I/me) experience collapses the whole chain going backward in time.

How do we know? These delayed choice events will be in the memory. Of course, the secondary collapse events are difficult to recall or verify, but the primary event has been verified via the onset of 40 Hz oscillation in association of the P300 readiness potential. Some of Benjamin Libet's experiments discussed below also prove this point of delayed choice.

Libet's Experiments: There is a 500 milliseconds time gap of preconscious processing before both our external and internal experiences

The neuroscientist Benjamin Libet also did some experiments with brain surgery patients, a series in fact, that seem quite paradoxical when you first look at them. Indeed, they raised a whole bunch of controversy. But you know what? These experiments find very satisfactory explanation when viewed from the point of view of primary and secondary awareness events of the preconscious as discussed in the previous section. You be the judge.

The point to discern is this: Do people experience a direct external stimulus and its memory elicitation (an internal stimulus) differently? Libet found a way to apply direct electrical stimuli to the somatosensory cortex in such a way that the subject had memory-elicitations that are similar in sensation to that of an external touch stimulus. In a paper published in 1979 in the journal *Brain*, Libet and his collaborators describe their findings.

These researchers found that these critical stimulations of the brain areas must be of a minimum strength and duration (the duration and strength depend somewhat on each other) in order to be felt. And then there's the surprise. For low stimulus-strength, the duration needed for the application of the internal stimulus is about half a second. Compare this with this fact: even a very brief and very weak external stimulus leads to a sensation – a felt event. But, why?

Clearly, from a quantum science point of view, a reasonable hypothesis is that whereas the external stimulus leads to a primary awareness event and irreversible collapse of the quantum possibility wave involving the external world, the cortical stimulations lead only to secondary awareness events. If this is so, it also makes sense to assume that the half a second (500 milliseconds) is the processing time of secondary awareness events; it is the time it takes us to become aware of a cortical stimulus at the ego-level.

There is more to support this conclusion. If a strong cortical (internal) stimulus is applied after an external skin-touch stimulus within 500 milliseconds, Libet found that it is able to mask the skin-stimulus – the secondary events of the cortical stimulus drown out the secondary events of the skin-stimulus. This phenomenon is called backward masking. The success of backward masking establishes that the processing time of secondary awareness events leading to a verbal report for both external and internal stimuli is just about 500 milliseconds.

Clearly, the backward masking phenomenon gives us definitive evidence that there is a 500 milliseconds processing time between a sensory stimulus and its awareness at the ego-level capable of verbal expression. But is there any evidence that there is actually a primary awareness event in the brain in the case of an external sensory stimulus in this line of experiments? There is.

Interestingly, in addition to the backward masking measurements, Libet and his collaborators did another experiment that is very puzzling until we invoke the ideas of the primary awareness event of delayed choice and delayed quantum actualization. To this experiment, which seems to deal with the subjective perception of time, we now turn.

Is there any paradox in the subjective perception of time?

Mental phenomena are experienced as conscious events in a space that we call our awareness (Sanskrit: *chitta)* or mind's sky. It is analogous to physical space and is related to it in the case of physical events; that is, events in awareness correspond to events in actual physical space in some intricate manner but are not identical to it.

Let's consider a far more difficult question: How does the time of subjective mental events relate to objective physical time of physical events?

The measure of subjective time is clearly different than the objective measure we use for our clocks; but that is a minor point. Is subjective time qualitatively the same as objective time? Do they pertain to the same directional arrow of time? Do events retain their sequentiality, same sequence of events, in their subjective perception? These are questions that also give rise to paradoxes from a materialist perspective.

The greatest difference between objective time as defined by physics and subjective time is that the former is of a static characteristic but the latter is dynamic. Objective time in physics is treated quite symmetrically with space; space goes both ways and time does the same according to the equations of physics, Newtonian or quantum. There is no one way flow of objective time. The events of the universe are laid out in a canvas of static space-time so to speak. But in the subjective time that we experience, time flows, and flows one-way.

There are theories in physics that accommodate a unidirectional flow of time. For example, one invokes the idea of entropy (the amount of disorder) increase of the universe as a result of physical processes to give us an arrow of time. But the irreversibility of the entropy arrow of time is only apparently permanent, an appearance of irreversibility arising from the overwhelming probability in any event of collision for the occurrence of "nothing special" final states of which there are so many, compared to a "very special" orderly initial state. If we wait long enough, nothing in the physical laws prevents us from getting back to the initial state.

In the consciousness-based interpretation of quantum physics, the arrow of time finds a simple explanation. We discussed this in a previous chapter. This is because when consciousness collapses the quantum possibility wave (of a system or of the entire universe), there is real irreversibility brought about by the quantum measurement itself. Remember the necessity for a memory apparatus to be an essential part of the tangled hierarchical collapse that manifests the world in our experience?

In quantum science, the static time of physics belongs to the transcendent domain of possibility as a parameter given to the possibility wave functions. Actualization or collapse marks the real time of manifest reality as we experience it. Hence, this subjectively experienced time has direction; it flows one way from the past to the future.

Now let's discuss the most paradoxical part of Libet's team's experimental results. Suppose we have two readily distinguishable cortical and skin stimuli; for example, suppose that the cortical stimulus simulates a touch to the right hand whereas the skin touch is applied to the left hand. Here is the surprise. If the skin touch is applied some 300 milliseconds after the cortical stimulus, and both take a 500-milliseconds processing time to arrive at ego-awareness and verbal recall, we would expect that the subject would report the sensation of the cortical stimulus first and that of the skin stimulus some 300 milliseconds later. What Libet and his team found is that the subjects invariably refer the external touch stimulus back to its time of arrival at the cortex (which is only 10 milliseconds after the touch) and report it to have occurred first, even before the cortical stimulus.

There is something strange about this result if we think that the events are perceived in the same way irrespective of the event being internal or external. The subjective sequencing seems to be reversed compared to the objective sequencing in the laboratory of the time of application of electrical internal cortical stimulus and the external skin touch.

But there is no paradox when you use the primary and secondary collapse model and the idea of the preconscious, that is, the entire quantum science model presented here. There is no primary event of collapse for a cortical stimulus, only secondary awareness events. In Libet's experiment, when asked about the timing of the external stimulus, subjects correctly refer back to this primary awareness event, thus establishing its presence and timing. But subjects cannot similarly refer back to anything for the cortical stimulus that stands out and tells them about the timing of it. Naturally, they think that the skin touch occurred first.

There's one more important point to note here. *What cognitivists call brain acting in the unconscious mode due to the activation of unconscious memory are really preconscious imperiences.*

Why is all this important to know? A theoretical model of science applied to one situation must be applied to many other situations in order to prove its consistency. All these experiments described in the chapter, especially those by Libet and his team, proves the validity of the tangled hierarchy model of quantum collapse at the primary level, and simple hierarchical collapse at the ego level and the preconscious in between, all beyond any reasonable doubt.

On a personal note, I (Amit) was giving a talk at the University of Oregon in some department. After the talk a young man came to me and introduced himself. "You mentioned Benjamin Libet in your talk. He is my uncle." Oh, yeah. I was excited. Would he mind forwarding my work to Libet and get his comment? Of course, he wouldn't, the young man said enthusiastically. However, I never did hear from Libet. Perhaps quantum science was too far out for him to comment. You have to remember! This was very early days of consciousness research – the nineties.

Qualia Again and Oneness of Experience

There is a unique quality to a conscious experience – eating a banana and talking about it are not the same thing. Indeed, a philosopher named Dunne questioned back in 1927 how physics could ever explain to a born-blind person the experience of seeing light. Dunne insisted that the quality of an experience can be understood only by direct experience. The experience of light does not reside either in the light waves or in the receiving apparatus – the brain. Let's elaborate on this idea; let's examine the response of the brain upon receiving a stimulus.

There are now experiments suggesting that a stimulus is processed in several brain areas. In the first area, a direct one-to-one representation of the object is made. For example, for a visual stimulus, the primary occipital cortex plays this role. In a second area, the brain performs an analysis of the stimulus involving massive amounts of neurons. For a visual stimulus, this is done in the secondary and tertiary occipital cortex. Similar primary, secondary, and tertiary areas also exist in the temporal (auditory) and parietal (somatosensory) lobes. In still another area, the associated area of the cortex, the analytical representations from the various areas seem to be integrated.

What happens in this area of integration? Whatever happens, we know the result since we know that there is always a unity of the resulting experience. The result of the integration has to be the production of a neuronal field, an electrical image of some kind.

Suppose the stimulus is a red car with its engine running and you let several people experience the sight and sound and touch of the car. Suppose also that you have available to you the right combination of some super technology and high-power mathematics that you are able to make a complete description of the neuronal field of the brains of your subjects, even one for your own brain, upon experiencing the car. Except for minor differences, you would expect the neuronal fields of all the brains, including yours, to be identical.

And yet, you know that in the case of your brain, something is left out, something that the objective neuronal field cannot possibly describe, and that is your subjective experience as observer. You might say that the neuronal field of your observer brain is special compared to all the observed brains. But then you would be admitting (barring solipsism – the idea that only you are conscious, others are robots) that your conscious experience of your brain state changes your supposedly objective brain state. The alternative is to admit that the neuronal field does not provide complete description of the experience. Either way, the problem of qualia is a thorny paradoxical problem for the materialists. Some philosophers, Daniel Dennett for example, negate the notion of qualia altogether.

The quantum science's theory of perception successfully eradicates the paradox of qualia of experiences. Because consciousness of the experience transcends the brain, the neuronal field unifies the disperse activity of the brain, but clearly is an incomplete description of the experience which must include the feeling connected with the movement of the morphogenetic/liturgical fields associated with the neuronal field. And then there is the mind giving meaning to the various potentialities that the neuronal field presents to consciousness for choice. Consciousness chooses the field that makes the perceived image meaningful. And the subject pole of the conscious awareness of the experience arises co-dependently and tangled hierarchically, as the meaningful neuronal field possibility becomes actualized as the faithful meaningful image of the physical object of perception. Concommitantly, the chosen vital possibility actualizes as the felt quality of the experience; and all this without dualism.

Let's repeat. The idea of consciousness tangled hierarchically actualizing both the neuronal field and the feeling-quality of the experience also resolves the thorny issue of the oneness of a conscious experience (that we can be consciously aware at any given instant of only one particular thing). It is well-known that all attempts by psychologists and neurophysiologists to split the unity of a conscious experience (for example, by surgically splitting the brain hemispheres) have failed. In the quantum scenario, there is only one actualization at a given time, and that defines the event in awareness.

However, the memory of secondary awareness processes of two primary events can overlap in time. This is responsible for the fact that we can be vaguely aware of several things in awareness at the same time.

Thus, we can see that an understanding of all the different aspects of the qualia of experience can be obtained within the extended context of the quantum paradigm that consciousness connects to the material world using the intermediary of the subtle. We do not need to resort to negate qualia altogether as materialist philosophers like Dennett do in desperation.

We know there are the three normal states of consciousness – waking, dream, and deep sleep – that everybody experiences every day and that are all essential for everyone. However, an important question of the science of consciousness to be addressed is this: Is there any data to support that people can attain exalted states of a variety of spiritual experiences that people all over the world have reported from time immemorial? Have neuroscientists been able to ascertain the claim of these people? Fortunately, there are such spiritual people even today who have experienced exalted states and they are not even very rare. And yes! The neuroscientific data also exists and looks promising: meditation data. So, what does the data tell us?

First of all, when we say meditation, what are we talking about? Concentration meditation – concentrating your attention on an object, external or internal, helps you to take you and your brain away from me-centeredness. Another way of meditating is variously named as mindfulness or awareness meditation, witnessing meditation, or meditation on the subject. You become mindful of what his happening right now; you just pay your attention to awareness of whatever object arises in awareness without judgment. Gradually, you settle down as a witness of both the subject and the object of awareness that is taking place. This meditation is also about present-centeredness.

The early data during the seventies and eighties going into the nineties mainly consisted of brain wave data. The research proved several things that got widespread attention. Meditation produces relaxation and the immediate proof of that is the dominance of alpha waves (frequency 7.5 Hz to 13.5 Hz) in the meditative state and this is reached quite easily. Deeper meditation leads to dominant theta waves of even lower frequency (3.5 Hz to 7.5 Hz) suggesting deep relaxation.

Long-term meditators of mindfulness meditation show two more interesting characteristics:

1. Their overall reaction time to external stimuli is much reduced maybe by as much as to 200 milliseconds reaction time compared to the average person's 500 milliseconds reaction time to respond. In other words, the brain indeed slows down through meditation. In this way, long-term meditators are privileged to enter what we ordinarily relegate to the preconscious. And indeed, they see the world as more alive because of the increasing proportion of the "I" of the quantum self in their experience.

2. Long-term meditators do not habituate to repetitive sounds like a clock ticking suggesting that their alertness, attention level, has increased.

There is much more data now to complement the brain wave data – functional magnetic resonance imaging (fMRI) data. As we have said before, neuroscience is changing; many neuroscientists recognize the shortcomings of material monism and are eagerly contemplating a new science that would include spirituality and with that in mind they are using the new imaging techniques of neuroscience to explore the brain area correlates which are involved in spiritual experiences. One of these researchers is Andrew Newberg, who earned quite a bit of stir with his books *Why God Won't Go Away*, and its sequel, *How God Changes Your Brain*. Another researcher of note is Mario Beauregard, author of the book *The Spiritual*

Brain. Still another is the pair Daniel Goleman and Richard Davidson who wrote the book *Altered Traits*.

We have already spoken of the regions of the brain involved with the ego-persona that neuroscientists refer to as the self-agency. When we perform willful actions, the attention takes the brain activities from the region of self-agency to task-related regions of the pre-frontal cortex, each task taking up a specific area or areas. And when we don't perform willful action, the brain goes back to its default area. You can think of the default area as the vegetating "me" area; much more of the cortex become involved in the more present-centered task-performance; think of it as I/me area for the experiencing subject. In our ordinary task-related situations, the brain fluctuates between these two areas.

Since meditators motivated toward higher states of consciousness are engaging in willful action, Newberg says, the initial stages of their meditation must involve the prefrontal cortex, and neuroscientists find that indeed is the case. And since attention is involved, the brain area called Anterior Cingulate cortex (ACC) should become involved, says Newberg. This, too, is indeed the case with meditators of higher consciousness.

One important word of caution about what popular wisdom tells us about the milestones of spiritual advancement that mystics warn us about all the time. But regardless of the warning, popular wisdom and human nature like to emphasize them. Nowadays neuroscience research is confirming the old saying, "If you see Buddha on the road, kill him." The discussion above should convince you that deep meditation only leads you to states deep in the preconscious, more and more into the quantum self, but seldom fully there. A genuine quantum self-experience leading to insight the manifestation of which is transformation, would require a quantum leap of creativity after a sustained application of the creative process. However, one does occasionally fall into the quantum self from these preconscious states reached by meditation. And this means that these visions that we see in meditation are projections of the preconscious editing coming from these occasional unintended forays in the quantum self that takes the meditator to collective unconscious experiences. They are significant of course; they are confirming that you are getting deep into the preconscious, which is good.

Another important word of caution: Neuroscience is also telling us that experience of ecstasy reported by many meditators are due to the ample presence of the neurotransmitter molecule of dopamine, the same molecule responsible for ecstasy upon the intake of cocaine. Again, ecstasy is good, but there is nothing much to really crow about if a drug can give us the same experience.

Traditions like some forms of Buddhism try to claim big transformational change out of preconscious states reached by meditation. More recently, some transpersonal psychologists, notably Ken Wilber, have made the same mistake. The message of the quantum worldview and neuroscience data is clear: meditation is good practice but it is nothing but preparation for transformation, real change. Real change requires sustained application of creativity, a stage-by-stage process that includes two-level (conscious and unconscious) processing and discontinuous big quantum leaps, followed by a manifestation stage. In the manifestation stage, there is intense interaction between the ego and the quantum-self that psychologists call flow and people experience it as a flow. You can think of flow consisting of little quantum leaps of inspiration in otherwise continuous ego operation that we call perspiration. In this way, you can think of creativity culminating in a big bang followed by many little bangs so to speak. In view of the brain data on the preconscious, you can also think of flow as the experience of the preconscious.

The important thing for you to know and get motivated is this: The quantum leaps of insight followed by transformative manifestation do produce increasing levels of happiness and intelligence; this is all scientific and quantifiable.

Questions to Ponder Upon

1. Ponder the distinction between conscious, unconscious, and preconscious.
2. The idea of two-self modality of the brain, one personal, one transpersonal and spiritual, is now established as a scientific aspect of human nature. See that this is an immediate validation of the fundamental principle of ethics: it is important to be good to others. How do you think this should affect moral development of children since quantum self comes to them quite often?
3. How do you think the idea of two selves should change capitalistic economics and business practices?
4. Debunk the theory that the readiness potential proves unconscious brain action in your behavior.
5. Ponder about the arrow of time and how its traditional explanations fall short, and how quantum measurement theory as explicated in this book gives the definitive solution to another outstanding problem

of physics, namely, how time gets its unidirectional nature, its arrow.

6. We have given several ways to look at the flow experience. Which of the way/ways resonate with your own experience?
7. Think about subjective qualia and its explanation. Compare with your own experience.
8. Practice both concentration and awareness meditation and ponder on its effect as you compare notes with the data in this chapter.

CHAPTER 7

States of Consciousness

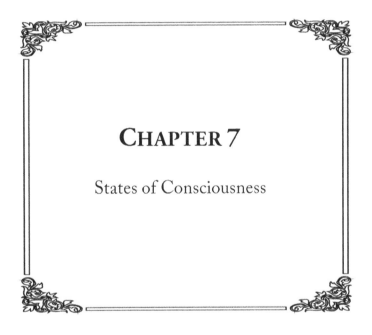

Brain waves are a measure of the average state of oscillation of the various regions of the brain organs. Human experience corroborated by brain-wave data (fig. 12) allows us to enunciate the three major states of consciousness:

1. The waking state: Here we have both external and internal awareness. The brain waves range from alpha (7.5 Hz to 13.5 Hz) when we are relaxed, to beta (13.5 Hz to about 30 Hz) when are doing a task, and gamma (30-100 Hz) when we are super attentive and present-centered invoking the quantum self.

2. The dreaming state: Only internal state of awareness exists. The rapid-eye-movement (REM) is the give-away signature of the dream state. The brain waves are dominantly theta (frequency range of 3-7.5 Hz).

3. The deep sleep state: Here there is no subject-object awareness at all, no collapse of the possibility waves. The brain waves are low frequency delta (1 to 3 Hz); the brain is mildly active with unconscious processing of its memory. However, which part of the memory is being processed while we are sleeping? The quality of sleep can have an answer to this question.

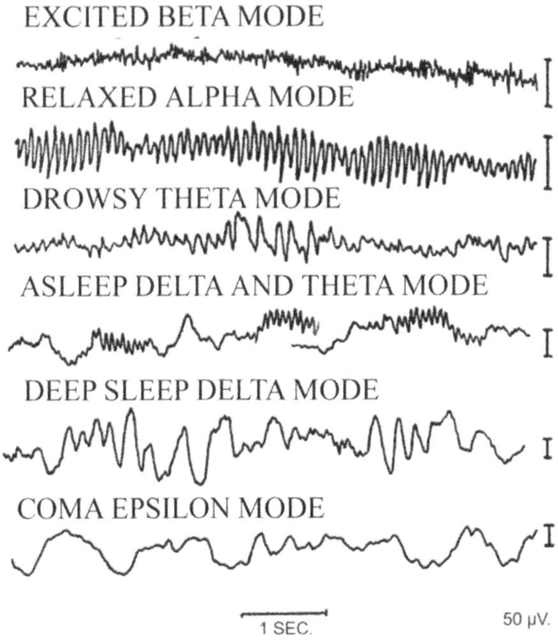

Figure 12. Brain wave data for different states of consciousness

In the normal waking state of our self we call ego, we become preoccupied with the external world so much so that we become quite unbalanced between the external and the internal, producing the internal-external dichotomy. Today we belong to an information processing culture; the information we thrive on are all about the material world of samsara which further enhances the dichotomy. Suppressing emotions does not help either.

Hence, we need to rewire the brain, build new circuits of meaning processing and create new meanings to explore, engage with pure feelings in the body, and explore the archetypes. This will help balance inner and outer, transcendent-immanent, and male-female dichotomies.

The dreaming state is entirely about our meaning life; it is an ongoing report of the meanings that need to be addressed in our waking lives. Paying attention to dreams helps us not only explore meaning but also further balance and integrate the inner-outer dichotomy.

As we integrate the inner and the outer, dreams help us in our exploration of the archetypes and creativity via archetypal dreams that Jung called big dreams that come with archetypal symbols.

We can be creative in both our waking state and our dream state in dreams called lucid dreams. If we live our creative insights thus achieved, we make in the brain positive emotional software that not only helps us balance the negative but also helps us integrate creativity and conditioning, yin and yang, or transcendent and immanent. This is a major aspect of brain rewiring.

Deep sleep is also very important to us and to our brains; the organs connected with self-identity need much rest, that's one reason. In between sleep and wakefulness, we have the drowsy state with its own brain wave signature of theta waves of frequency between 3 and 7 Hz.

In the awakened state, when we become sensitive to feelings and wake up the latent navel and the heart chakras, we notice another dichotomy. This is the male-female dichotomy: women have strong heart, much other love but not much navel identity, or weak self-respect. Males the opposite: strong navel, weak heart chakra identity. Male-female balancing gives us a strong self of the body that spiritual traditions call spiritual heart; it is called so because it is easy to connect with the spirit (quantum self) from this state. When we balance the head with the spiritual heart, it is a major optimization of brain function.

II Non-ordinary Expansive States of Consciousness Including the Fourth Major State Called *Turiya*

Recent neuroscience research has already given us evidence for other evocative states of consciousness:

4. Flow state: A state of consciousness in which we experience a high dosage of the quantum self while engaged in ordinary tasks so much so that accomplishing the task seems effortless. The brain signatures of this state are: preponderance of gamma waves and non-local synchrony between distant areas of the brain.

Flow states are most well-known in sports. Ball players talk about being in the zone, golfers too. Their flow, as well as the flow that singers, dancers, and musicians experience, is a combination of mastery and letting go. The complete mastery lets one relax to the extent of falling into the quantum self and get into flow.

The flow experience is also an ingredient of the manifestation stage of the creative process.

5. The Creative "aha" State: The state of surprise of the discovery of an archetype in its suchness reached via a quantum leap of fundamental creativity. It is a transient state. Its signature is gamma burst.

Additionally, mystics talk about three more states:

6. *Savikalpa* (a Sanskrit word meaning with separation) *Samadhi*, samadhi with subject-object separateness: In ordinary experience, there is subject-object split of the Oneness, but the object dominates. Samadhi means the two poles of subject and object are

experienced equally; in other order words, the experience is one of approximate oneness of the subject and object, of their co-arising.

Like the creative "aha" experience, this state is also transient and super-conscious and has the same brain wave signature—gamma burst.

This *savikalpa* state of spiritual experience in terms of the language of creativity theory is the result of a creative quantum leap revealing the archetype of self. The difference from other creative archetypal experiences is this: since the self is the objective of the exploration, when the quantum leap occurs, the true nature of the subject – Oneness – is revealed; there is no individual self. In this way, the experience is one of Oneness and the world on equal footing. Hence the name, *samadhi*. And the experience is: oneness of everything.

7. *Nirvikalpa* (Sanskrit for no-separateness) state of the lower kind: This is a state of *Samadhi* without subject-object split. Mystics claim that it is possible to "be" in the unity consciousness, the ground of being directly at equal footing with and retaining one's potential identity and there is much potentiality for experiencing joy in attaining it. This fourth major state of consciousness is called the state or *Turiya* in Sanskrit. Like deep sleep, this state is unconscious in us. However, in deep sleep the unconscious we are in is our personal unconscious of brain memory, whereas the unconscious in *Turiya* is the unconscious of never before manifest potentialities, an unconscious that we call quantum unconscious.

When people wake up from the state, a state sometimes called superconscious, mostly they talk about experiencing a kind of joy called *Turiyananda* – limitless joy.

In normal deep sleep, the brain waves do their waving with delta waves of frequency 1-3 Hz. Neuroscientists have discovered a deeper state of sleep in which the brain waves at <1 Hz. These brain waves are called epsilon waves. It makes sense that in this state, cortical neurons not only are unconscious but also the mental memory possibilities connected with them are no longer processed even in the unconscious. In this way, the existence of such deep state beyond ego signifies spiritual attainment of much non-attachment. But such a brain is still alive, because the vital brain is still processed in potentiality. The cortical brain cells involved with the vital brain are likely to be the glia – white matter.

Here is enlightened philosopher/mystic I personally knew, Franklin Merrell-Wolff talking about his quantum-self experience in savikalpa samadhi as an experience of complete freedom:

The first discernible effect on consciousness was something that I may call a shift in the base of consciousness…*I knew myself to be beyond* space, time, and causality…*closely associated with the foregoing realization there was a feeling of* complete freedom…*I did not attempt to stop the activity of the mind, but simply very largely ignored the stream of thought. The result was that I was in a sort of compound state whereas I was both here and "there," with the objective consciousness less acute than normal.* (Franklin Merrell-Wolff, *Philosophy of Consciousness without an Object*, pp. 38-55)

Neuroscientists may have found a brain-wave signature for this *savikalpa samadhi* state as well: the lambda wave of frequency >100 Hz. In Franklin's experience, his brain was going and forth between the lambda mode and the beta mode.

8. The sages of Vedanta and Buddhism claim that there is a state of consciousness higher than even the *turiya* state only that you cannot talk about it. They maintain that "being" in that higher *nirvikalpa* state is different from all other being; it has no qualifications, there is nothing to talk about. So, this state is called the Great Void or *shunyata* (nothingness) in Buddhism and *Nirguna Brahman* (Brahman without qualifications) in Hinduism.

Each of the first seven states mentioned above has its own brain wave signature and so do some of the other states of no subject-object split, such as a coma or people under anesthetic. The very last state (#8) of non-dual consciousness is not expected to have any brain signature.

The task of theoretical neuroscience is clear: to explain all these states of consciousness, everything that is possible for the mind to experience. Throwing doubt about the veracity of creative flow and mystical states of enlightenment is not science because the empirical data already pass the test of weak objectivity. Science's job is to provide theories and then develop new protocol for experimental investigation of what is already part of the empirical data of consciousness studies. This is the objective of quantum neuroscience, as you will see as it develops. Amazingly, a few neuroscientists have already taken this task seriously and it is heart-rending to see that.

While neuroscientists do their job, it is up to you to scale these mountains of heightened consciousness. The authors believe in quantum activism, an activism to "be the change I want to see in the world." From this perspective, the optimal goal for any human being living in the world is to achieve the state of flow in any task he or she is engaged in. This is the ultimate goal of optimization of the function of the brain as well.

The phenomenon of trauma has much importance in children's and adults' psychological well-being. We discuss it here because the phenomenon further supports the already proposed mechanism behind our negative emotional brain circuits.

Let's discuss the mechanism involved in trauma associated with life-threatening incidents such as terrorist attacks, sexual assaults or violent personal attacks.

First, consider the brain mechanism involved from conventional neuroscience, that is, material monism point of view. According to this view, brain does everything, partly unconsciously, and partly with awareness. In all traumatic events, the brain takes in sensory information, and relays it through the thalamus. The thalamus, bypassing the neocortex, sends sensory information to the amygdala where the information is scanned for danger. If the amygdala senses the danger, it activates the motor organs. In this way, the unconscious processing of the mid-brain initiates the fight-flight response. At some point, the neocortex enters the picture, and we begin to experience changes in our body such as the heart beating faster and the lungs taking in more air.

The important thing is this. Whilst the amygdala has been set-off by the traumatic stimulus, the hippocampus which is responsible for memory processing, organizing and sequencing events shuts down. Therefore, memories of traumatic experiences are stored without the full context. This is why people who experience trauma cannot remember the full sequence of events or they may only recall "fuzzy memories."

The issue that the traditionalist view creates is that if the memory is stored without the full unconscious context, then the brain doesn't have the information about how all the sensory information fit together when the experience occurred. This means that in future the amygdala could very easily be triggered if it detects any of the aspects of the previous traumatic stimulus.

For example, let's assume that somebody is sexually assaulted, and the attacker is wearing a red shirt. Because the victim is undergoing the fight or fight response, the hippocampus has been shut down and hence the brain isn't able to record everything that happens in proper sequence. A few weeks later, the victim is out shopping, sees some lady wearing a red top, and experiences a severe panic attack. The red top alone has triggered the amygdala into setting off the fight-flight response. Because the hippocampus was not able to store the memory in the full context, the amygdala precipitates action albeit there is no real threat – it only associates the red top with danger and hence responds. And all of this may happen with the brain in the unconscious mode. So, the victim may not even know what triggered the response.

Apart from the unjustifiable assumption that the amygdala can cognize by itself, the other crucial question here is why does the hippocampus go benign while the amygdala is active doing its thing?

Now let's reconstruct this scenario into a quantum science version assigning the brain-vital brain combo as the provider of possibilities for consciousness to choose from, and with the idea that there is unconscious instinctual memory of feelings at the amygdala that plays out in response to a stimulus, but collapse can take place only at the vital level via the vital self at the midbrain. However, this is quantum-self experience, and most people would not be aware of the feelings nor of any secondary collapse events, they remain in the preconscious. Only later when the neocortex comes into the picture and gives meaning to the feelings, do we have conscious experience. The imperience is collapsed on a retroactive basis and becomes new unconscious memory. In this way, the hippocampus and new emotional memory-making happens only after the neocortex enters the picture and not when the amygdala was doing its thing.

As we said before, unconscious or preconscious memory cannot be recalled at will and reinforced. However, since an external stimulus is involved, we remember that collapse event, but vaguely, since there were only feelings to produce the cognitive experience. The memory is fuzzy with no sequencing for which we need the mind and the hippocampus. And it is this fuzziness of memories that robs the victim from the ability of proper sequencing of the events and so a little part of the original stimulus is sometimes able to evoke the entire memory with dire consequences.

Near-Death Experiences

Some people after a cardiac arrest die clinically (as shown by flat EEG reading), only to be revived a little later through the marvels of modern cardiology. Some of these near-death-survivors report having witnessed their own surgery, as if they were hovering over the operation table. They are uncannily able to give specific details of their operation that other witnesses verify that leave no doubt that they are telling the truth, however difficult it is to rationalize their autoscopic vision while dead.

Well, they are not "seeing" with their local eyes, with signals – that much is clear. Indeed, even blind people report such autoscopic vision during their near-death coma. These patients are "seeing" with their non-local, distant-viewing ability using the eyes of others involved with the surgery – doctors, nurses, etc. But this is only half of the surprise that the data present.

Try to understand how these people can "see" even non-locally while they are "dead," unconscious, and quite incapable of collapsing possibility waves and making cognition and memory. Unconscious processing, of course, is available; the brain memory is gone but the collective unconscious and its non-local memory are still there to provide internal stimuli for thinking in potentiality. Indeed, the descriptions near-death survivors give – meeting relatives, spiritual figures and Jungian archetypes, celestial light – fit the images available in the collective unconscious.

The rest of the mystery is solved by invoking that most amazing quantum phenomenon – delayed choice and delayed collapse.

NDE as Delayed Choice

In a near-death experience, the delayed choice and collapse takes place at the moment the brain function returns, as noted by the EEG, precipitating a whole stream of collapses going backward in time.

Beside autoscopic visions, NDE survivors report seeing archetypes of the collective unconscious. Since they are unconscious at the time, we must distinguish this kind of delayed choice experience happening in retrospect from normal experience. Earlier, we have called them 'imperience'. Imperiences are potentialities that are collapsed by delayed choice.

A New Insight: The brain dies momentarily, yes; but the NDE cannot happen while the brain is dead

In my (Amit's) previous work, I always thought this explanation so far is adequate to explain everything about NDE. Actually though, one thing is still missing. The retroactive events of delayed choice collapse in their own time. How do we know that they did happen? The proof is memory, we remember. But for NDE, where is the memory made? The NDE survivor's brain is not available during the time of the near-death experience in conventional wisdom.

Comments by the neuropsychiatrist Bruce Greyson of the University of Virginia:

The primary challenge in the study of NDEs and spirituality lies in asking how complex cognition, sensory perception, and memory can occur under conditions such as cardiac arrest in which current physiological models of the mind [consciousness] deem it impossible.

This conflict between a materialist model of the brain-mind (consciousness) identity and the occurrence of NDEs under conditions of general anesthesia and/or cardiac arrest is profound and inescapable.

Even with use of quantum science, the conflict remains. I think now is the time when the conventional wisdom about NDE needs to be changed and replaced by another. Namely, with the beginning of the cardiac operation, at some point, the NDE survivor's brain does return some functions among which are cognition and memory. This is when near-death imperiences take place. Still no collapse is possible at the ego level until the brain is restored more fully. In this way, both mental thinking (with the help of internal stimuli from the collective unconscious and brain memory) and brain cognition and memory-making go on in potentiality, and they all collapse retroactively when conscious awareness at the ego level returns with adequate brain recovery.

It fits. In autoscopic experiences, the NDE subject picks up other people's cognition of his surgery non-locally, but how does he remember this, how does his brain make that memory to remember? It had to be alive with the memory-making capacity available in potentiality. Furthermore, although the images of the collective unconscious dominate the descriptions survivors give of their NDE, there is also plenty of scope for mental imagination. The memory thus recorded in a recovering brain of an NDE survivor should be fuzzy (as in a trauma) and the NDE survivors fill in a lot of the fuzziness with imagination.

Questions to Ponder Upon

1. What do brain wave data tell us about the possible states of consciousness?

2. Many people think meditation takes us to altered states. Ponder how. What do you think meditation does to our brain?

3. Ponder about how you experience inner-outer, creativity-conditioning (yin-yang) and male-female dichotomies. How do you think you can integrate these dichotomies? Do you want to? Will these integrations optimize your intelligence? What do you think?

4. Think about this question: Can we have delayed choice experiences without the brain? Do you agree with the conclusion reached here?

5. What is a *samadhi*? Ponder over the distinction of *savikalpa* and *nirvikalpa samadhi*s. Do you feel inspired to explore the whole gamut of state of consciousness available to all of us?

CHAPTER 8

The Brain and Reincarnation

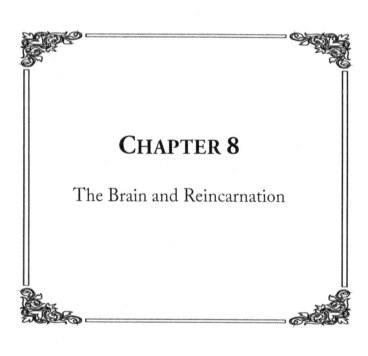

Cell biology has a general problem: the problem of heterogeneity. If a living cell multiples and generates an entire colony, the members of the colony develop heterogeneity. But all the cells have the same genes; so, if genes determine everything, then how come heterogeneity? Realizing that a cell has memory since it cognizes its environment solves the problem. Memories will in the least carry different personal qualities of feelings in reaction to the environment resulting in somewhat different response for a learned stimulus; this creates different vital memory to live by for each cell of the colony; so there will be some heterogeneity.

Materialist neuroscience suffers from the same problem with heterogeneity albeit to a lesser degree since different brains have different genetic composition at least. Still, the biological functions of the brain organs and the universal liturgical software that comes with each are all the same. So, how come there is heterogeneity? The general answer is again the same: memory.

Materialists generally assume that whereas nature – the genes – determines the hardware, it is nurture that is primarily responsible for conscious memory and software. In this model, kids growing up under the same socio-cultural conditioning should have just about the same emotional and mental software. And of course, our whole educational system counts on that: schools teach the various subjects of education in the same sequence and at the same rate. There are some exceptions made for the talented and gifted.

However, school administrators are aware of one thing: not only the rates of learning are different for different kids, but their emotional and mental software is also different, often in a significant way. Can little difference in the kids' nurturing account for this much heterogeneity?

Quantum science scientizes a different source of memory that Eastern yoga psychology has been telling us for millennia – reincarnation.

Reincarnation

Religions claim survival after death. The near-death experience verifies this claim. Some religions claim reincarnation – we not only survive after death but are reborn in another body, live another life and die only to repeat this death-birth-rebirth cycle.

In a consciousness-based science, consciousness always survives, that is not the question here. The puzzle is, can your personal consciousness, the ego, survive death, even be reborn?

This question seems to counter science when you first examine it. The brain is a must to create the ego. All those memories that make up the ego, don't they vanish, gone with the wind when the brain dies?

Not so. Much data now exists for survival after death. Hard to believe, but people who are called channelers that claim to temporarily embody these discarnate beings were once the butt of everybody's jokes, but now they have been studied by scientists and their work have been validated a lot. Even mediums who claim to mediate communication with the deceased are gaining respect. What gives?

Ian Stevenson, who was a psychiatrist at the University of Virginia Medical Center, single-handedly made the idea of reincarnation a legitimate scientific idea by validating reincarnational memory recall by children all over the world.

In 1998, I (Amit) went to speak at a conference where I encountered the research of the famous parapsychologist Stan Krippner and his collaborators on the channeler JZ Knight. These researchers had measured eight psychophysiological indicators and found that these indicators read differently when JZ is channeling compared to when she is just her. Go figure.

The hardware remains the same while channeling; the difference must be coming from the emotional and mental software. During channeling, the channeler is using a different emotional and mental software. That she is using the emotional and mental software of the channeled entity makes sense.

It checks out. Later research by the parapsychologists Norman Don and Gilda Moura on a famous Brazilian medium demonstrated that while channeling, this medium's brain waves change from the normal beta mode to the unusual gamma mode of frequency higher than 40 Hz reserved for unusual people, people of high capacity for concentration or people having flow experience, for example. Indeed, the channeler claimed to be channeling a surgeon and was performing surgery on people while channeling! So, the emotional-mental software of the channelers do change while they channel. How come?

In 2001, I wrote a book called *Physics of the Soul* in which I demonstrated that the substantial defining part of what we call our individual ego/character/persona consists of stuff that can only be called non-local memory. Nonlocal as you know exists outside of space and time. So, this finding of the quantum science is reviving the ancient Hindu concept of *akashic* memory which is the basis of the Hindu theory of reincarnation.

The Sanskrit word *akasha* means outside space. If memory is non-local, people residing all across space and time can share the memory. You can be like an individual pearl in a string of pearls of many incarnations in your past and in your future.

So, what is this defining part?

Karma

What reincarnates? Our mental body that we mainly identify with, consists of three things: 1) subtle declarative meaning-memory correlated with brain memory; 2) ego conditioning consisting of functional propensities that make up our habit patterns and character traits; and 3) personality programs that the ego controls. Of this, numbers 1 and 3 are local, but quantum physics suggests that #2 is non-local memory. Thus, this non-local memory not bound by space and time, is what goes with us when we die and reincarnate in our future incarnations. These propensities are called by the Sanskrit names *karma* or *sanskara*. Please note that this is not the today's conventional meaning of *karma* as a recurring cause-effect or action-reaction relationship between people lasting over incarnations.

Same kind of consideration should hold for our vital body/physical and vital/mental (that is emotional) software. The emotional character or learned propensities via the processing of feelings is what reincarnates. Read my book *Physics of the Soul* for more details.

So, the puzzle of the channeling data is also solved. Since I live in Oregon, and JZ lives in the state of neighboring Washington, I did one more thing. For a couple of years, I used to speak at JZ's ranch giving myself the opportunity of studying the phenomenon of channeling up close.

Indeed, I discovered things in general agreement with the idea that a channeler's character changes while she channels. I found that the channeled entity Ramtha's character is different from JZ's. The content of what Ramtha said during popular presentations comes from JZ's brain-mind including all such mythology that made Ramtha popular, such as Ramtha was a 35000-year-old soul from Atlantis, such as Ramtha was the *avatara* Rama in India. Nowhere was this verified better than the following incident.

One time I gave a talk at the ranch about the double slit experiment. Imagine my surprise when the very next day, the double slit experiment was the main feature of Ramtha's presentation! Pray tell: How does a person who lived 35000 years ago know about the double slit experiment?

We discussed near-death experiences in the last chapter. Apart from Jungian symbology of the collective unconscious if the reincarnation model is correct then there should be also elements of personal non-local memory in the NDE. There is. NDE survivors always claim that they see relatives. If you see a relative in a dream that generally means the aspect of your character and habits that this relative represents. It must be the same way in NDE. Our character and habits represent us when we die.

Reincarnation aficionados please note: this is probably not the way you think of reincarnation as a surviving entity living a dead brain and re-entering an aborning brain. Please discard that old image. Note that even the propensities that you inherit from past lives do not activate at once. They have to be triggered by the circumstances of your current life as they occur.

Brain Data for Nonlocal Memory: Lashley's Experiment

There is direct brain evidence that suggests that the memory of a learned propensity is non-local. In the nineteen fifties, the neurophysiologist Karl Lashley did an experiment in which he was trying to study the location of the memory of the learning of a propensity in the brain. So, he trained rats to find cheese in a Y-maze (putting electric shock at the other prong of the Y) and then systematically began to chop off parts of the rats' brain and test the rat's behavior to see if the propensity remains. Strangely, he found that even with 50% of its brain removed, a trained rat finds its way to the cheese. The only valid conclusions are: 1) A rat's learned memory of a propensity is not just sensory but sensory/vital (since the rat cognizes and learns through feeling); and 2) the sensory/vital memory is not localized in the brain, and instead is non-local *akashic* memory.

II Yoga Psychology Gives Us the Important Concepts of *Gunas* and *dharma*

Reincarnational history contributes two other specific new aspects which are important for human development. These two aspects are conceptualized in yoga psychology with Sanskrit words – *guna* and *dharma*. Let's talk about *guna* first.

The concept of *guna* is misunderstood even by most Indians, unfortunately. Probably when it comes to their cultural heritage, everyone, including scientists, become conservative. Ever since its early days, millennia ago, the Indian Hindu culture became moribund with only occasional flurries of dynamic activities due to the brief appearance of a mystic who set things straight. You have to understand Hindu concepts and how people interpret them today from that context in mind.

Gunas are qualities of our subtle bodies. This much everybody agrees. Why are they important? When we try to make a science of the concept, it becomes obvious. They are qualities arising from how we deal with our vital and mental bodies over our many incarnations. How do we? Grossly speaking, as the Chinese do, either we concentrate on *yin*, the potentialities reached by stillness or on the *yang*, the movement in what is already manifest. The former makes you creative, the latter emphasizes on conditioning.

Conditioning is an easy quality; it maintains status quo, and resists change; this tendency comes to all of us naturally. That is how we begin life's journey through all our incarnations. Then, only when we feel higher needs, for example when we get bored with the old or when we cannot find peace with what we already have, we try the path of creativity.

For creativity, we can get little more specific. Creativity can be used in two ways – situational and fundamental.

You want to expand your consciousness and learn ethics – how to love your neighbor? You find your particular answer by exploring creativity with the context of Christianity that Jesus prescribed two thousand years ago. It still works. The Sanskrit word for this way of using creativity is called *rajas*. You may be familiar with the word *raja* which means king. After conquering one land, kings of the old used this kind of creativity when they wanted to go on conquering. Each land requires somewhat different strategy, but the conqueror always went forward with the same overarching goal – empire building. As you learn ethics – being good to others with situational creativity, you may be encouraged to explore justice – being fair to people – the same way. That would make you a *rajas*-dominated personality.

But there is also a more ambitious way to be creative. Why not include even the archetypal context within the fray? Times change. Physical environment, society and culture all change. When you explore the archetype itself to discover new meanings and feelings with the objective of discovering a new face of the archetypal context, you are engaging fundamental creativity.

Thomas Kuhn discovered the concept of paradigm shift in the sixties. Science undergoes a revolution when the archetypal context of exploring truth – the scientific overarching law comes into question as to the extent of its validity. Such a paradigm shift occurred with the quantum laws of physics replaced the Newton's laws. This is fundamental creativity.

The capacity for using fundamental creativity in our creative exploration is called *sattva* in Sanskrit; this exalted quality enables us to explore and embody the archetypes.

The Gunas and Doshas (see below) are described here somewhat differently, giving them more meaning than what you may find in the spiritual traditions or even in Ayurveda. I (Valentina) am using these concepts not only as part of diagnosis, evolution and treatment of disease but also as spiritual growth evaluation. We hope you will benefit similarly from our viewpoint here.

Tamas – conditioning – is ever present; it is a price we pay for growing up and cluttering our brain with all sort of memories. So *tamas* dominates when we begin our reincarnational journey; we settle for *tamas* because we don't know any better. Only gradually with some incarnations completed on our string of pearls, conditioning gives way to creative tendencies of *rajas* (propensity for engaging situational creativity); and *sattva* (propensity for engaging fundamental creativity) comes into the scene only after many incarnations of *rajas*-dominance.

Our place on the spectrum of intelligence depends crucially on the *gunas* we bring with us when we incarnate anew. For most people even today, for the vast population of underdeveloped countries, the dominant *guna* is *tamas*. The more *rajas* we bring, the more we desire to achieve. This is the case in economically developed countries such as the United States and developing countries such as China, Brazil, and India.

The more *sattva* we bring, the more is our tendency to delve into fundamental creativity, and eventually engage it for emotional well-being and positive mental health in search of enlightened living. How much *sattva* or *rajas* or *tamas* we can bring to bear in this life depends on our reincarnational history.

In this way, reincarnation theory tells you a very important thing: know your predominant *guna* before you engage in development as an adult – personal growth work. Likewise, educators and our educational system must make adjustments for the difference of inherent *guna*s among their pupils.

Doshas

The reincarnationally inherited *guna*s affect the brain's software development of the current incarnation; this is their importance. In our developmental period of childhood and early adulthood, sometimes we use excess, too much of a particular *guna* in exploring emotions and meanings. This produces defects of the physical organ software called *dosha*s in Sanskrit. If you use your vital *guna*s in an unbalanced way while you grow up, you develop vital-physical *dosha*s that pertain to the physical body organs, and are a basic component of the ayurvedic medicine – *kapha* (due to the excess use of conditioning), *vatta* (due to the excess use of situational creativity and problem solving) and *pitta* (due to excessive use of fundamental creativity).

Likewise, excessive unbalanced use of the mental qualities produces *dosha*s in the brain-mind. Excessive use of fundamental creativity produces intellectualism – overvaluing mental intellect. Unbalanced use of situational creativity gives you brain hyperactivity, excessive fickleness. Excessive use of conditioning (avoiding creative challenges) produces the brain *dosha* of mental slowness, a dumbing down, sometimes leading to apathy, passivity, and easy manipulability.

These brain *dosha*s are important contributors to how we react to stimuli of negative emotions called stressors, how we handle emotional stress. In the West, the culture generally imposes suppression of negative emotions on people. However, we find some people, generally men, do get upset and express it; they are short-tempered and irritable. Further study shows that these are people of the hyperactive *dosha*. Intellectuals, on the other hand, quite successfully manage to suppress their emotions.

However, both habits take their toll. Expression and negative emotional experiences may give us heart disease. Suppression is even responsible for cancer, although cancer can result from certain types of expressive personalities as well. Read Amit's book, *The Quantum Doctor*, for a detailed discussion, and the upcoming book written by us, *Quantum Integrative Medicine.*

Is there a better way to handle negative emotions? Yes. Meditation. With some practice it works.

III How you get Your Personal Archetype called *dharma*

We spoke of evolution and purpose before. Is there a specific form that our purposiveness expresses itself in our lives? Yoga psychology says yes. Each one of us who has been on the reincarnational journey for a while picks up the idea that life is most meaningful when we pursue new meanings (and feelings) in new archetypal contexts. Since exploring an archetype is time-consuming, naturally we adapt a specific learning agenda for each incarnation, to explore only a few archetypes. In yoga psychology, this leaning agenda is called by the Sanskrit word *dharma* spelled with a lower case 'd.' This is to distinguish dharma from *Dharma with capital D* which stands for the totality – Brahman, or the Chinese concept of Tao.

For normal functioning, if you are not interested in personal growth, you don't necessarily need to know your *dharma*. But if you are an "old" mature soul and are ready to explore archetypes, it helps to know it. The reason is that life becomes full of satisfaction if we follow our own learning agenda.

The concept of dharma is an important part of the reincarnation theory. It is amazing that today everywhere people use the concept of *karma* but the concept of *dharma* has yet to enter their knowledge horizon. Our *karma* has two parts: some of our habit patterns and character traits that we bring with us from our past incarnations are survival oriented; they give us quick survival ability. But there are others, sometimes we summarily call them good *karma*, and that is where the key of our purpose for this incarnation lies. These we bring in order to explore our *dharma*, to build our purposive future.

Why Children of the Same Culture Grow Their Brains Differently

Let's return to the issue of children's heterogeneity. We humans are basically all the same; otherwise, talking about a common human condition makes no sense. The organs, amygdala, hippocampus, the organs of the coveted neocortex, all do their basic functions the same way. This is the universal portion of the brain software. This part of brain development suggests homogeneity of human beings.

But there is another part of development. We interact with our environment, both non-living and living, we feel and we think. This creates software/memory in the brain. This software is widely different between different humans. The biologist/author John Medina, in his evocative book *Brain Rules*, explains and we will paraphrase slightly marked by brackets:

Even identical twins don't have identical [soft-] wiring… [Suppose] one of the twins earlier in the day reads a magazine story about panned action movies, a picture of [Halle] Berry prominently on the cover. [The other twin] doesn't read any such story. Then they both watch a Halle Berry movie Cat Woman. If we could put microelectrodes in their brain and could see and interpret how their brains were rewiring, we would observe that the brain [of the magazine-reading child] is busy comparing and contrasting comments of the article and the movie and is assessing whether he agrees with them. The other twin has not seen this magazine, so his brain isn't doing this. Even though the difference seems to be subtle, the two brains are creating different memories of the same movie.

Today neuroscientists can put microelectrodes in an epileptic child's brain and can map it while doing a task; so, the thought experiment is not that far-fetched. And when you consider that while growing up, every twin goes through thousands upon thousands of such instances you accept that basically the same cultural experience would create different software even for identical twins.

So, neuroscientists generally agree that cultural conditioning is overrated in terms of producing identical conditioning. Every brain's personal software is individual.

However, nobody can argue that the culture nevertheless has an overriding influence. It is the job of the culture to determine what kind of environmental and learning stimuli the children are exposed to and approximately at what age.

But in actuality, this is not optimal to the child's situation. The strange thing is that contrary to prevailing assumptions, some children do not develop the ability of learning a specific area at the specific age that all children are expected to do in our educational system. In fact, the neuroscientific evidence is clear. Each child optimally learns specific areas of expertise in wildly different ages. And this one is hard, nay impossible to explain in a conventional manner why there are such subtle differences in creating the actual memory that produces the learning.

For connoisseurs of reincarnation theory, the explanation is obvious: the difference arises because children have widely different history of past life incarnations that are triggered at widely different age. Some are old souls, who naturally would be very good at basic reading, writing, and arithmetic having developed the expertise in their karmic repertoire. The authors know; they may be such old souls; they both learned the three R's at an early age, defying the norm.

All the discrepancy we see in the learning rate in today's children may be due to this reincarnational factor. Of course, materialists would bring up the genes, but let's face it: it takes epigenetic software to activate genes.

The discrepancy is mainly due to the different "good *karma*" that different children bring from past lives, those children who are at a stage of personal growth to have chosen a *dharma*.

So, neuroscientists are on the right track. It is the developmental psychologists and educators who have to make major adjustments in their methodology as our society becomes aware of what the new quantum science is telling us. Apart from nature and nurture, another factor – reincarnational history which is widely different from one child to another – also plays an important role in a child's development.

Lisa Miller's Work

The consciousness researcher Lisa Miller's experiments using fMRI seems to confirm what we are saying. Miller discovered that people may live different modalities of their brains. For the many ordinary people she studied, their pathway of brain activity follows motivation to reward circuit in the prefrontal cortex to pleasure circuits in VTA. But she also studied people who are born in spiritual/religious families. Their brain modality is different: the pathway involves not only the prefrontal cortex but also the parietal lobe where the processing is more holistic. And in general, for these latter people, more brain areas than just the self-agency and the task areas are involved when they do routine things.

Miller's interpretation is correct: spirituality produces transformation that involves the second non-local mode of operation of the brain. However, she theorizes that these people's genes are different and that is all there is to this data. This is similar to the old Galton theory of creativity genes. Reincarnation is a better explanation.

Similarly, family constellation therapy has revealed that traits go from one generation to the other sometimes in a line that can be traced through many generations. Obviously, the genetic factor gets more and more diluted as you come down a family lineage. You share half of your genes from your parents, but only one-fourth of the grandparents, and one-sixteenth of your great grandparents. The truth is, about thirty percent of people who are born in a spiritual family is spiritual. This is hard to explain on a purely genetic basis. Moreover, as we have already argued, genes need epigenetic vital software for suitable activation. Spirituality produces that vital software.

I think there is no need to assume that there are "creative" or "spiritual" genes just because there seems to a hereditary element in traits that continue in a family constellation. Instead, we can think in the reincarnational way. It is a part of reincarnation theory that in the initial stages, people will repeatedly reincarnate in the same family. So, if someone develops a particular software – good or bad – it will recur in the family because the same people will reincarnate in subsequent generations. Add some environmental influence propagating from one person to the next generation and you have got a pretty powerful scheme for propagating traits through generation after generation.

One more comment of enormous importance in passing. You know, when we theorize about personal growth for adults which is a matter of lifelong learning, we make the same mistake. Researchers in general fail to account for child development and the stages of personal growth for adults, because so far, reincarnation has not been considered seriously as an important factor in child development even by transpersonal psychologists.

Questions to Ponder Upon

1. Do you understand the concept of non-local memory? Pay special attention to the message of Lashley's experiment; this will help. Did you have a childhood talent that may have come from reincarnation and non-local memory? Think about it.

2. The definition of *karma* given here is different from the one you may be used to. If this is so, give some thought to this new way of looking at it and get used to it.

3. Dwell on the concept of the *gunas* and try to assess your own guna situation. Which of the *gunas* dominate you? Would you like to develop more *rajas* and *sattva*? Think of practices that may help you.

4. Knowing your *dharma* should guide your rewiring and optimizing your brain. Do you agree? Think.

5. Do a meditation of about 15 minutes daily for two weeks with the objective of remembering your childhood talents and propensities that may have gotten lost in the process of growing up.

6. Do a memory research on yourself, and chart how your professional interests and hobbies have changed over the years.

7. What is your current profession? Does it satisfy you or is it just a vehicle to make a living? Look at all the

jobs you have ever taken and see which one made you the most content?

8. Make an intention for a dream that will tell you your *dharma* for this life. Sleep with a notebook and a pencil handy so that you can write down a thing or two to remind you of the content when you wake up in the morning. Do dream analysis with a friend for a few months.

CHAPTER 9

Taming the Brain's Pathological Tendencies

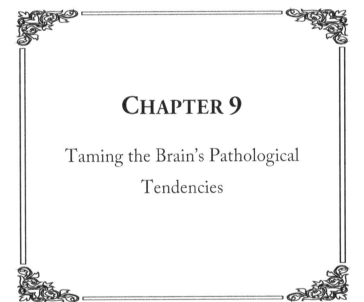

Brain gives us hardware which we can use according to the laws that govern us. These laws are laws of consciousness-based quantum science; that means these laws explain and preserve the basic properties of consciousness, two of which are freedom of choice and creativity. These laws also give us the sensitivity to process not only new external stimuli but also new internal stimuli. The latter comes as the experience we call intuition; the forever new stimuli we call archetypes.

When we say there are infinite potentialities for us to explore and take the homeostasis of human living to further and further heights of happiness and intelligence, it is the infinite potentialities of archetypal exploration and their representation via the mental and the vital to which we are referring.

The evolution of the brain's genetic hardware is over; however, during evolution of the genes, there was also simultaneous evolution of the vital software. Whereas the former is "Darwinian" and genetic, the latter is Lamarckian and epigenetic. We call the latter development; what it developed is what we call universal software.

Since genetic variations and environmental catastrophes are based on chance, the evolution of life is opportunistic, not programmed to produce perfection as religionists assume. To sum it up, the result has been that the current universal software of the human brain is far from perfect.

It is the effect of the imperfection of the universal software that influences how we grow our individual personal software that we need to tame. There are four major imperfections that define our base-level human condition: 1) machine-like information-processing tendency; 2) "me"-centeredness; 3) negative emotional brain circuits; and 4) pleasure centeredness. These tendencies are the biggest barriers to our creative exploration of the archetypes. They are also self-limiting; they create barriers to self-exploration as well.

During development of the human being from childhood to adulthood, these barriers to creativity and access to consciousness lead to the development of previously mentioned brain-mind *doshas*: mental slowness which can also be called "dumbing down" is likely a contributing cause for autism; hyperactivity leads to the pathological condition of Attention Deficit Hyperactive Disorder (ADHD); and intellectualism that can lead to depression and other pathology.

The negative emotional brain circuits can produce emotional stress. This combined with the *dosha* of hyperactivity leads to emotion expression and can also cause heart disease. Emotional stress is suppressed by intellectuals; it produces immune system malfunction and that can lead to both cancer and heart disease, even Alzheimer's disease when you recognize it as an auto-immune disease. These we have discussed elsewhere. Read our upcoming book, *Quantum Integrative Medicine*.

In chapter 9, we discuss the prevention of some of these pathologies during child development. We will also discuss how addiction can be prevented with proper child development. In the following chapter 10, we discuss taming the normal human condition to make room for creativity and transformation.

Autism is increasing at an alarming rate, according to Autism Society Canada, and may have doubled in the past decade. About 105,000 Canadians have an autistic or other developmental disorder, and 3,000 new cases were diagnosed in Canada alone in 2002. Statistics from school boards in Saskatchewan, British Columbia and Quebec show an average increase in autism cases of 63% over the last two years. Experts see no clear reason for the increase. The answer appears invisible only because it's too close for us to recognize it.

Is autism a genetic disorder or a developmental one? Some researchers flatly declare that autism is a disorder of development, characterized by impairments in interpersonal and social interaction and communication, along with rigidly repetitive and apparently purposeless behaviors such as tics (in quantum science we see these as involuntary vital energy release). Some neuroscientists, however, are prone to consider autism to be a genetic predisposition.

Autistic children display: 1) a general lack of social interaction ability that extends not only to adults but also to other children, even children of the same age; 2) slow cognitive abilities in both thinking and feeling. 3) They do not bond intimately with anyone, including their mother.

Some neuroscientists attribute the lack of social ability to the lack of mirror neurons. This could be a structural hardware problem due to some genetic predisposition. The other attributes are clearly related to child's personal developmental software and his/her abilities to use the software. Interesting enough, I (Valentina) have found autistic traits also in adults, and even more in closed spiritual communities. Dr Gabor Mate's research explains a lot about this as well.

Autism is a whole spectrum of disorders, but the essential quality of it is an emotional disconnect. These children are living in a mind of their own. They don't respond appropriately to emotional cues. They withdraw. They might act out in an aggressive and sometimes just unpredictable fashion. They don't know how to associate with others – there's no clear sense of emotional connection or peace inside them.

We have to realize that, whatever's going on, it can't be some "genetic problem" because genes don't change in a population over 10 years, 20 years, 30 years, or even 300 years. So, whatever is going on, it is not genetically determined. It may be biological, but it's not genetic, because we can't reduce biology down to genetics. There are also development and epigenetics.

We think it's a matter of connection rather than mirror neurons that is lacking in autistic children. On the neuroanatomical level, the brains of children with autism have reduced connections between important emotional centers and other brain regions. Psychologically, the autistic child lives in a world of his own, largely isolated from emotional contact with those who love him.

Such disconnect, though to lesser degrees, is also a feature of the many other developmental disorders now afflicting burgeoning numbers of children, including Asperger's syndrome, Tourette's and attention-deficit disorder. We all know the frustration, and even rage, we can experience when we make a phone call and instead of getting a responsive human being, we are greeted by a mechanical recorded menu.

Such frustrated rage at this disconnect is the constant emotional realm of the autistic child.

How Does the Disconnect Happen?

The physiology of brain development can no more be understood in isolation from the environment than we can explain a flower's growth without reference to soil conditions or climate. Even more than the flowering plant, the human brain develops in interaction with the environment. Genes, while important in their own right, are activated or turned off by developmental software – both universal and personal.

Ninety per cent of brain development occurs after birth, during the first two or three years of life. It is during this time that the genetic material is triggered to express itself in healthy or in disordered ways in the developing software.

Input from the nurturing environment heavily influences the chemistry of the brain, the growth and interconnections of neurons, and the development and interconnectedness of brain regions. The most crucial of these inputs are the subtle and often unconscious emotional interactions between the infant and his caregivers. To comprehend what is happening to the brains of children, we need to look at what has happened to the child-rearing milieu over the past few decades.

Fewer children today have the luxury of being born into a non-stressed, emotionally balanced and nurturing environment that the optimal biological development of the human brain requires.

But in some cases, parents of children with autism and other disorders do not love their children any less than other parents; they are not less skilled or devoted to the parenting task. Some researchers therefore suggest that to explain the explosion in childhood disorders we need to look at broad social factors, and not just at individual parental failure.

Throughout human evolution, children have been reared in the context of strong emotional relationships, in what may be called the "attachment village." In tribes, clans, villages, communities, neighborhoods and in the clasps of the extended families, children were assured of the nurturing influences necessary for healthy brain development.

That emotional nexus is, with catastrophic rapidity, disappearing from our lives. Tribes, clans, villages, communities are things of the past. We are less and less connected to our neighbors, extended family or fellow workers, even to our own spouses.

Recent economic, social and cultural changes mean the family is functionally less and less intact. Parents are increasingly stressed and isolated. If the emotional connections in our children's brain are not as developed as they ought to be, it's because the social connections on which they depend have been greatly weakened. Perhaps the autism epidemic is due to all this change in social norms, from the ones based on emotionality to others based on information processing and intellectualism!

As the physician Gabor Mate points out, the modern society's family structure of overworked parents and overlooked kids is an indication that the "it takes a village to raise a child" model is extinct.

There's a new theory for the autism epidemic that hearkens back to the "refrigerator mother" theory that autism is caused by cold, emotion-withholding mothers. The Albany Times Union reports that Dr Gabor Mate believes that parental stress, especially the mother's, causes developmental disabilities. Author of four books that explore the connection of mind, body and stress, Mate asserts that "the electrical circuitry of a child's brain is programmed by the mother's emotional state." But Mate has no explanation of how that can be.

Here, quantum science can help.

Quantum Theory of Autistic Disconnect

We, humans, cannot feel connected to a machine because local interactions with them do not lead to a non-local oneness. It takes intention to make a non-local correlation with another human being. A machine cannot intend. This intention is what the autistic child lacks; somehow his or her intention about connecting to the rest of the world is switched off; it has become machine-like in that respect.

There is an abnormal state of humans – clinical depression – when this kind of intention switching-off does happen. If this kind of depression happens to a woman with a more than sixteen-weeks-old fetus, what then? The fetus and the mother's brains are non-locally one with one difference: each of mother's state that collapses as an experience remains uncollapsed in the fetus' brain; these uncollapsed states can only collapse after the fetus is born.

There was a study recently that showed an increasing number of men are having pre- and post-partum depression, as well. And the main role of the father, of course, would be to support the mother. The cause of depression in the mother is not necessarily intrinsic to the mother – it could be the lack of support from the father. What we have to understand here is that human beings are not discrete, individual entities, contrary to the free enterprise myth that people are competitive, individualistic, private entities. What people actually are, they are social creatures, very much dependent on one another and very much programmed to cooperate with one another when the circumstances are right. When that's not available, if the support is not available for women, that's when they get depressed. When the fathers are stressed, they're not supporting the women in that really crucial bonding role in the beginning. In fact, they get stressed and depressed themselves.

The important thing though is to recognize that the child will inherit some of its software from the mother, including the willful exclusion of socializing or connection-making intentions.

Add to this the grim scenario of today's child-rearing for working mothers. Most mothers are forced to go back to work very soon after childbirth, long before the child has any idea of a personal thinking self. When the child's cognitive ability is entirely based on feeling, the child spends much time going back and forth between the quantum-self and the developing individual ego. There is a very important phase here of child development: connecting with mother. Mother is gradually replacing the quantum self during this phase. If this transference does not take place, the child's development may be affected. And this may very well happen when a mother leave a less-than-a-year old child in a child care facility.

Any chance of recovering from the disconnection that took place unconsciously in the mother's womb via conscious experience of motherly love and re-connection is also gone if the mother is not available. In this way, the disconnection becomes very deep and inaccessible in a full-blown autistic child.

There is really no quick way for parents to break though such disconnection once it has happened except to transform and develop their own capacity of unconditional love. Autistic children are in their brain a lot. With unconditional love, if you bring the energy of your child down by Tai Chi style palm movement from the brow chakra to the heart chakra, the child's response may surprise you. But this requires you to have the patience of a saint!

A much better strategy is to change the current disconnected social norm to one with a lot of quantum connection. It is true that we cannot go back to old-fashioned joint families, when somebody or other would always be there to care for a pregnant woman's emotional mood swings when the husband is not available. But we can easily create internet groups and use the group bonding to care for pregnant women. To create such support groups is part of our quantum activism movement.

Mental Slowness, Reincarnation, and the Phenomenon of Idiot Savant

Apart from parental and social disconnect, the other dominant aspect of the autistic personality is mental slowness, repetition of meaningless tasks, etc. And then there is that astounding phenomenon called Idiot Savant: suddenly the child finds an area of interest, his abilities develop quickly in exploring the new avenue, and the child becomes a genius while still maintaining the social disconnect.

The two phenomena – mental slowness and Idiot Savant – may be related. The explanation is to be found in the concept of reincarnationally inherited qualities – *karma*, *guna*, and *dharma*.

Karma is non-local memory of propensities of habit patterns and character traits we bring from our past lives. Some of the good *karma* we bring is to facilitate our exploration of a chosen archetype or *dharma* for this life.

Guna represents the specific mixture of conditioning and creativity that we bring to bear in our current life. If a child's early life is full of challenges that she is encouraged and inspired to engage in, she would use a healthy mixture of both creativity and conditioning. If such stimuli are lacking as well the inspiration from the environment, what then? Imagine being an autistic child already emotionally disconnected from the world of relationships and also lacking in stimuli that would trigger her interest, the archetype of her choice! This would only augment the rage she feels from the disconnect and she would be prone to withdraw from the world even further.

If however, perchance, new stimuli do appear with such force that her archetypal memory is triggered, she can wake up to all those propensities and character traits she has brought with her. That is the phenomenon we call somewhat derogatorily as Idiot Savant.

What's a parent's strategy then to grow a child so there is no encumbrance to curiosity and interest? Obviously, parents, and then educators must cater to the possibility of multiple intelligence, the fact that many people, girls for example, speak in languages that are different from that of the intellect.

Other Factors: Trauma

Many other things make sense as factors in the rise of autism – environment toxins triggering genetic propensities for instance.

Research does, in fact also suggest that childhood trauma influences a child's developmental success and failure, affecting both their mental and physical outcomes well into adulthood.

We must add trauma as one of the contributors to how autistic children lose connectivity.

Traumatic events in childhood have a huge impact upon the life course of an individual. The more traumas a child endures, exponentially greater is the amount to expose him later on to not only sufferance, illness, ADHD, anxiety etc. but also autoimmune disease and cancer.

Realize! Trauma is not the bad things happening to you but what happens inside you as a result of what happened to you. Trauma is an overwhelming threat you don't want to deal with.

The first thing that happens as a result of a traumatic incident is that you separate from a part of yourself. So, trauma fundamentally means a disconnection from the whole self. Why do we get disconnected? Because, it's too painful to be wholly ourselves.

The child's brain development depends on the presence of non-stressed, emotionally available parents. All over the world today, that kind of parental support is less and less available. The parent's insensitivity to the child's emotions sets up a cognitive dissonance in the child's brain producing a traumatic memory because of the lack of time-sequencing about such events. Hence, you've got burgeoning rates of autism in the upwardly mobile intellectual middle class everywhere. It's going up like 20- or 30-fold in the last 30 or 40 years.

In fact, human biology and human neurobiology are interpersonal. The brain is a social organ, and it's affected by the environment, and particularly it's affected by the psycho-emotional environment. So, then you have to ask: What might be happening in society that might be affecting infants and children?

To emphasize once again: the essence of trauma is disconnection from a part of ourselves. Trauma is not the terrible things that happen from the other side – those are *traumatic stress*. But the trauma is that very separation from the body and emotions. Trauma sets up an interior castle in people. For normal people with a traumatic memory or two, the castle is hardly noticeable by people in superficial relationships.

For autistic children that castle covers virtually the whole being; it is visible.

So, the real question is, "How did we get separated and how do we reconnect?"

Our true nature is to be connected; a baby is born that way. In fact, if that wasn't our true nature, there would be no human beings. The human species or any species in fact, could not evolve without being grounded in their bodies and its quantum vital connection. You couldn't have a bunch of intellectuals walking around out there in the wild, wondering in an abstract sense about the meaning of life, when there's a saber-toothed tiger lurking behind the next bush.

It's not an automatic outcome of living in the world that we should become disconnected. It's a product of a certain way of life and a certain way of parenting and certain childhood experiences, where it becomes too painful to stay connected so disconnection becomes a defensive maneuver.

The way back to wholeness is impossible under materialism, because the essence of materialism is to think of consciousness as a product of the body. And, basically, in that view people are all considered material machines. People matter only because they produce, consume, or own material stuff. If you don't produce, consume, or own matter, then you don't matter in this society. We have to recognize the severely prohibitive limitations along with the great achievements of this particular way of life. It's not a matter of providing some utopian prescription.

On a personal level, it's a matter of deep self-work. One thing we've done now with the new quantum paradigm is a lot of brilliant, necessary research about what trauma is and how it shows up in the form of physical and mental illness and alienation and disconnection from other people and from yourself. And a lot of complementary work has been done on the reversal of trauma and the healing of it – and also on the prevention of it. But, again, it is not easy to apply that new knowledge based on quantum science; the social structures are not ready.

Medical students and psychiatrists, for example, are not allowed to learn this new quantum science in their academic training. Most physicians don't even hear the word "trauma" in their education and they have no understanding of it. Every time they see somebody with an autoimmune disease or other mind-body illness, they're looking at somebody who's traumatized, but they don't realize that. So therefore, we deal only with the physical manifestations, but not the actual causes.

To move forward, we have to have a society that is guided by the research that is already extant. So that anyone who deals with children needs to know the simple facts about the importance of relationality and brain development, and teachers need to be much more involved in relational activity with their students than in getting facts and information across. The curious, motivated student will want to know the facts intentionally, so they're easier to teach. But when kids are troubled and alienated because their relational needs have not been met, and you try to hammer information in their heads, it's impossible.

So, the educational system needs to change and the medical system needs to change. How young families are supported needs to change. The barbarism of American policy around maternity leave has to change.

On the positive side, the human brain retains a capacity for development throughout childhood and beyond. Emotional connection is the key. The greatest successes in the treatment of autism rely on building and maintaining a secure and powerful emotional relationship with the child.

ADHD: *Rather than an inherited disease, Attention Deficit Disorder is a reversible impairment and a developmental delay, with origins in infancy. It is rooted in multi-generational family stress and in disturbed social conditions in a stressed society.* Says Dr. Gabor Maté, in his book, *Scattered Minds.*

In the United States, the attention deficit hyperactive disorder among school children has reached an epidemic proportion, some 15% of the population. What could be even worse is the response of the medical profession to this data. The pharmaceutical companies got into the act and psychiatrists today routinely prescribe stimulants to most of these hyperactive children that continues through their whole lives. And now we debate: What is worse, the condition or the pharmaceutical cure?

Psychiatrists, who are materialist scientists, generally believe that disease, both physical and mental, are biological in origin, and that means genetics to most. Fortunately, today, there are also biologists who are aware of epigenetics: that environment determines biological software. In this view, ADHD is not genetic in origin; it is a result of a child growing up through enormous environmental stress, both from family and society. We quote Gabor Maté again: *We're looking at the huge impact of the environment on the troubled functioning of many, many young people and children. And to reduce that to a question of brain biology and to try and smooth it out by medications is an abdication of medical responsibility.*

Maté's point is obviously well-taken. In quantum science, for the brain, biological software consists of universal vital and mental software, epigenetic, yes, but also non-physical and liturgical in origin. Under environmental stress, a child responds according to the universal software which is often not adequate to address the stress. The child then engages creativity to bring new morphogenetic/liturgical fields and new meanings into action, creating new individual emotional software to find adequate response to the stimulus, often engaging in overuse of creativity. If the creativity engaged is situational, the overuse leads a brain-mind *dosha* – hyperactivity.

There is also a vital side to the *dosha* development – excess *vatta*. The excess *vatta* explains why hyperactive children cannot keep physically still; they fidget as the vital energy finds release.

Hyperactivity that begins at an adult age may not have a brain-mind *dosha* involvement at all. It may solely the effect of excess *vatta* at the vital level.

In this way, use of psychiatric medication would be entirely inappropriate for these children and adults. The cure – lifelong stimulants – is not even necessary.

Meditation or slowing down the mind and *pranayama* or slowing down the vital is the obvious way to heal hyperactivity. Meditation, however, is hard to practice for hyperactive children. Certain *hatha* yoga postures however, are very effective to momentarily reduce hyperactivity to the extent that the child can sit quietly for a few minutes at a time, and practice concentration meditation and *pranayama*. Also, a lifelong prescription, yes. But it has no side effects. Instead, huge side benefits.

Quantum medicine practice is a preventive practice, we must emphasize. Current child-rearing practices are grossly wrong being based on outdated theories of the brain. If we use the ideas of the quantum brain to grow a child, hyperactivity can easily be prevented. A detailed discussion is beyond the scope of this book however.

"Nothing reflects the effects of a sad life as graphically as the human body," said Naguib Mahvouz, an Egyptian novelist.

Due to addiction, people lose their health, beauty, teeth, human relations, even life. Nothing can force them to give up addiction, it is so powerful. Why is that so? An addict said: "I am not afraid of dying, I am afraid of living". What is wrong and what is right about addiction? What does a person get out of addiction, if anything? A relief from pain, a sense of peace, a sense of control and power, and a temporary calmness. Why are these qualities missing from one's life? Check all drugs – heroin, cocaine, alcohol – they all are pain killers. So, the important question is, "Why the pain?" and not "Why the addiction".

A guitarist from Rolling Stones was a heavy-duty heroin addict for a long time. Addicts are looking for oblivion, not to be themselves, for a few hours. People use drugs to soothe their discomfort, with a desire to escape from their own minds.

There was a study showing what people are afraid of most: death, of other people, or of their own mind. Most people are simply afraid to be alone with their minds. And they distract themselves through work, shopping, music, consumerism, sex, internet, food. Dr Gabor Maté defines addiction to be "any behavior that gives you temporary relief, temporary pleasure, but on the long run causes harms and you can't keep it up due to the negative consequences."

Buddhists have the theory of the hungry ghosts – they can never get enough. All hungry ghosts have this emptiness inside and they are trying to feed it from outside. If you want to ask the question of why people are in pain, you should not look at their genetics, but look at their lives. They were abused all their life, sexually abused as children, neglected, physically abused, emotionally hurt over and over again, have been through pain. Human beings develop personal software for their brain from their interaction with the environment.

The environment that a child has will shape the development of her brain. I (Valentina) have first heard about this concept many years ago, when I was studying *Bardo Thodol*, the book of the dead.

Here are a couple of experiments with mice. You take a little mouse, you put food in his mouth, he will chew it, swallow it. But if instead, you put it down, few inches from his nose, he will not eat it. Dopamine flows when we are motivated, curious, when we seek for food or sex. When an addict seeks cocaine, they get dopamine in their brains. What happens in their brains? Drugs are not addictive by themselves, there are many who tried them and did not become addicts. Just like food or TV is not addictive to everyone. Why the susceptibility? Why some are vulnerable to being addicted?

Here is another experiment with infant mice, that when separated from their mothers will not cry for their mothers. In the wild, this means they would die, because a mother is meant to protect and nurture their life. Why don't they cry? Because genetically the researchers had knocked out the neuronal receptors, the chemical binding cites in their brains for endorphins, and endorphins are indigenous morphine-like substances. Endorphins are our natural pain killers. What morphine or endorphins also do is they make possible the experience of love, the attachment between parent and child, thus these little mice without natural endorphins receptors in their brains were naturally not calling for their mothers.

In other words, the addiction of these drugs and of course heroine and morphine act on the endorphin system. Psychoneuroimmunological studies have shown, endorphins are the brain's way of connecting to the heart chakra – the immune system, the suspension of whose me/not-me distinction brings you love. The question is what happens to people that they need these chemicals to find love?

In conditions of abuse, for children, these important receptors and brain circuits just don't develop properly and their brains become susceptible. When they do the drugs, they feel normal, they feel relief, they feel love. One of Dr Maté's patients said: "When I first did heroine, it felt like a warm soft hug, like a mother embracing their baby".

Because of their non-local connection, babies pick up the stress, the terror, the depression of their own mothers, and that reshapes their brain with software that says – "the world doesn't want me, if mom is not happy with me". And then later, when they grow up, they become workaholic – "If they don't love me, at least they will need me". And in their turn, they will be too busy to entertain themselves to prepare for another day's job, ignore their children who will not feel loved and so on. In this way, we pass on trauma and suffering from one generation to the next. There is a different way to fill the emptiness, but the addicts never get a chance to discover that; it all goes back to what we didn't get when we were small.

There is also a great addiction to power, wealth, acquisition, for people who want to make themselves bigger than life, dominating others. For instance, Alexander the Great, Hitler (an Austrian not German), Napoleon, Genghis Khan – they were all small people and they all were outsiders, they were not part of the greater population – their only purpose was to conquer and maintain power. Addiction to power is essentially trying to fill up the emptiness from outside. Napoleon said, "I love power", he had no sense of himself without power gained externally.

Now compare these people with Jesus or Buddha – they were both tempted by the devil – the devil offered them power, they both said no, because they had the power inside of themselves, they didn't need it from outside. Also, they didn't want to control and dominate people, but to teach people through soft wisdom, love and persuasion, not force. Jesus said, "Power and reality is not outside but inside." Buddha, before he died said, "Don't mourn me, don't worship me, be the lamp unto yourself."

Trauma and Addiction

The problem remains in regard with behaviors categorized under one diagnostic or another – addiction, trauma, brain development. It is known that there is a great risk for cancer, addiction, mental illness, erectile dysfunction, relationship problems, personality disorders for people whose childhood was affected by trauma.

Academic pediatric study shows the development of a child: early childhood stress or trauma results in adaptations that help the child survive on short term but they are the basis of pathology later on.

The problem for the therapist is to remove an emotional block, not an intellectual block; there are enough studies that show that. There is no need of more research on what causes this, and bring more of the intellectual industries, knowledge factories to justify more jobs, but therapists should simply apply what is known.

This Is Known: Childhood trauma is a GREAT predisposing factor in addiction. There are hundreds of studies on the relation between trauma and addiction.

Quantum science tells us we have two selves: the quantum-self we are born with and then environmental conditioning gradually changes our everyday self-experience into an ego-experience. The quantum-self is non-local; the child misses it as the ego experience more and more dominates it; it has to find an attachment to another person – mother is the natural choice – to non-locally bond with and attach with to replace the missing quantum self.

The ego also needs to be authentic, to be in synchrony with the quantum self in order to have an ongoing presence of it in life at all. Competing with this is the relationship problem: if I'm authentic and express my feelings, my parents can't handle it. In this way, the child is forced to develop persona, a mask of inauthenticity that hides its needs, in the process often being traumatized and stressed.

Studies by Dr Gabor Maté confirm these findings of quantum science of child development. Read his book, *When the Body Says No*.

Spiritual Bypass

Meditation, yoga, chanting, prayer, community living – these are all sources of great comfort. But when we use our spiritual beliefs, practices, community, or way of life to help us avoid experiencing or processing emotional pain, we move into a state of spiritual bypass.

Spiritual bypass is when our practices calm the internal discomfort we feel –anger, sadness, fear, shame or self-loathing – but this doesn't actually help us to effectively move through it. The key is to uncover, process, and heal, so we can move forward in wholeness and freedom. What we need is transformation.

We will need to learn how to access and begin to heal early traumatic life events; get a better understanding of internal triggers and how they began; uncover the buried, unconscious feelings that hold us back; recognize the mental and emotional patterns that are limiting wholeness, choice, and freedom; trace and uncover repressed emotional states through body awareness; begin to establish balance within, so we can live our life optimally.

Distinguishing Pleasure and Happiness: Making the pleasure barrier as an opportunity for exploring happiness

The best way to deal with one major source of addiction or pleasure seeking is preventive. Can we train a child to see pleasure in a different light than just having a good time?

For most kids, food addiction is their first bout with addiction. If you see an obese child who also likes food, you can suspect that there is some pain that is leading to the pleasure-seeking. Is there a way to prevent this?

What happens when we eat food that gives us pleasure? Dopamine in the brain. Pleasure is molecular happiness. When we stop eating, another neurotransmitter comes into play: serotonin. This one is supposed to make us relax, eventually inducing sleep. But, you know, it is not quite like that.

Listen to an alternative scenario that quantum science gives: pleasure satisfies our survival need felt as self-gratification at the navel chakra. If you develop sensitivity to the navel, you can feel it, as can a child. In fact, it is easier for a child. The energy then tends to rise via the meridians that connects the navel and the heart chakra organs and activates the heart chakra. This expands our consciousness with a momentary touch from the quantum self, bringing relaxation. This then leads to emission of the neurotransmitter serotonin in the brain.

Suppose we change the usual way we eat and teach children to eat by our example. Suppose, instead of waiting for the serotonin to enter the picture after the meal, we serve the meal course by course! With a little waiting in between! At each break, there will be the following sequence: dopamine production stops, energy rises from navel to heart, and serotonin comes into play. But before the serotonin makes us sleepy, we start eating the next course. We go through the whole sequence again. You get the picture: do-be-do-be-do.

I (Amit) grew up in a lower-middle-class family in India. But even though we always had financial belt-tightening, my mother nevertheless insisted on serving a five-course meal. Imagine that. Only after understanding the quantum science behind it, did I understand the wisdom of this practice.

Italians are doing it now. They are bringing back their slow food tradition.

What the do-be-do-be-do way of imbibing pleasure does is to make pleasure into a doorway to happiness as well. There will be a noticeable difference. It is called satisfaction.

You know people often ask us about when they should teach their children about archetypes. Well, you have to teach by way of experience. Pleasure is insatiable; happiness satisfies. This is the fundamental difference between survival needs and higher needs. There is no way you can satiate your survival need; there is never enough security. But higher needs, archetypes, bring you satisfaction.

CHAPTER 10

The Base-level Human Condition and the Quantum Principles of Transformation

I (Amit) will tell you my favorite story from the Upanishads of India, very telling about how we can make changes, and one that I tell in quite a few of my books each time changing the tone to fit the context. I will make some introductory comments first.

Hindus call the fundamentally creative *sattvic aspect* of the human being *deva*. But overuse of it during ego-development produces intellectualism – a detachment from the body. Ideally, the *deva*-dominated people should look for the intuitive part of human experiences, but the problem is to get stuck in the mind's rational intellect. Too much analysis. *Deva*s also lack awareness of feelings in the body. That makes them vulnerable to emotions the way the brain processes them – pleasure and negative emotions. *Deva*s suppress the latter and indulge in the former a lot.

The situationally creative *rajasic* aspect of the human is called *danava* in Sanskrit. The *danava*'s problem is hyperactivity—fickleness. They express their negative emotion and are often cruel, violent, and dominating. And often they additionally learn to use their pleasure circuits in conjunction with their negative emotional circuits. In other words, they derive pleasure from other people's discomfort, the ultimate use of domination.

And the hierarchical me-centered apathetic ego-persona is called the human-person or *manava* in this story.

Here is the story. All three, *manava*, *danava*, and *deva* are tired with their brain-dominated limited rational intelligence loaded with negativity, superficial positivity of pleasure and sluggishness of the mind. They all want to change; they want real intelligence. One day, they see a strange being sitting on a hilltop, a being of considerable power emanating from it. Naturally, "Can this guy help me?" speaks up in each of the aspect of the human being in the form of the question, "How can I be more intelligent?"

First, the *tamasic* aspect of the human person: "How can I be more intelligent?" The being says, "Da." It is an intuition you see, subject to interpretation. The *manava* understands the intuition this way. Da stands for the Sanskrit *datta* meaning "give." The human-person is constricted by me-centeredness and apathy. Giving expands consciousness. This is like an initiation to the transformative path to higher intelligence.

Now the *danava* approaches and asks the same question. The being answers, "Da." The *danava*, too, understands this in his own way. To him, Da stands for the Sanskrit word *dayaddhama* meaning "have mercy." Cultivate positive emotions like compassion to balance all the negative ones. That will require creativity and transformation, too and will drive you toward higher emotional intelligence.

Finally, it was the turn of the *deva*. Same, question, same answer, "Da." The *deva* understands. For him, "Da" stands for the Sanskrit word *damyata* meaning "restrain." Restrain yourself from too much rationalization and too much molecular pleasure. Then room will be made for subtler experiences of feelings and intuitions, the creative exploration of which will bestow supramental intelligence.

Good recipes to be sure. But they are not compelling, nor do they do the job adequately. Can we do any better now some seven thousand years later? We have to; the society has changed.

Fortunately, our research and exploration of quantum physics and consciousness for four decades tell us yes. We can.

II What Does Quantum Science Say about the Journey of Transformation and the Awakening of higher intelligence?

What would quantum science say to the question of transformation? Let's first take up the case of the *manava* in us. Today's *manava* has an additional problem that increases the constriction of consciousness: too much information processing. Too much use of machine intelligence and too little of human contact; let's call this condition *yantrava* (*yantra* means machine in Sanskrit). So not only the *manava* has to expand his consciousness but also has to shift his interest from information to meaning in order to graduate to human intelligence. Develop positive feelings in the body, understanding other people's meanings and developing personal meanings, the currently forgotten part of human intelligence.

Giving is an excellent recipe for expanding your consciousness and in quantum lingo it takes you to discover in yourself an aspect that you thought you lost since childhood: non-locality. Why is that uniquely important for transformation? Non-locality helps us see the unity with others. Non-locally correlating with others expands our consciousness to inclusivity. As we include another in our consideration of living options, we are being "good" to the other, and we feel good – a positive emotion.

The quantum worldview says, we human beings have the potentiality of being one with everybody else using this non-local communication. Naturally cultivating non-locality will help to reduce your "me"-centeredness and open you to positive emotions.

In the brain, your "me"-centeredness expresses itself as vegetating in the brain areas that neuroscientists identify as belonging to the self-agency. The reinforced memories of ego-persona that feed your "me" are stored in nearby areas. In the body your self-centeredness expresses yourself as vitality tied up to the navel chakra – the welfare of you and you alone. Narcissism. Or for women, in the heart chakra. Too much neediness, needing another to attach to.

Giving, giving unconditionally, obviously takes you away from the thoughts of the "me"-personas. It also raises the energy from your navel chakra to your heart chakra (for needy women, the movement is from the heart to the navel). Why? Giving makes you aware of the archetype of love and goodness which you represent as other-centered thoughts and noble feelings.

Giving is just one practice; another practice you can do is the practice of not taking yourself so seriously – humility. Still another one is forgiveness. All these practices also help one to gain access to positivity that is not pleasure.

And then one can give up information processing to avoid boredom and concentrate on meaning. This begins with understanding; bring your own meaning-giving capacity of the mind to play. Once this becomes fun, one can develop an interest in the archetypes and delve into personal meaning explorations aplenty. This is human intelligence of normal level.

Transforming the *Danava*

And now we can address the *danava* in us, the propensity of situational creativity. In the quantum worldview, creativity is synonymous to discontinuous movements – quantum leaps – of thoughts and feeling.

A quantum leap is a regular fixture of the quantum worldview. It is via these quantum leaps of thoughts and feelings that you not only make positive emotional brain circuits but also add a new trait to your character, the ability to balance your dominant negativity with your newly gained positivity.

Situational creativity is creativity within a fixed archetypal context given by somebody else, perhaps a teacher, or a good book. It is about finding new meaning and feeling to represent the archetype, within that given archetypal context, new meaning and feeling that you embody.

Imagine exploring compassion within the context that the Bible gives: love your neighbor. So, your neighbor is a man, and he wants a cup of sugar. Jesus gives the recipe: if somebody wants one shirt, give him two. So, you give him two cups of sugar. But suppose he comes back the next morning again; he is out of sugar. Old stuff will come up: will he ask me sugar every morning? Will this fellow reciprocate if I need something? It is this old pattern of thinking, your old character that you are trying to replace with a more compassionate character. Work on opening your heart and search for new meanings for what comes up.

To open your heart even to this extent you have to discover feelings in the body and their body centers – the chakras. You have to discover that if you are not so miserly, so anal retentive, the energy from your lower two chakras do not always collapse in the navel. Sometimes, they go all the way up to the heart and collapse. That's when you get the feeling of compassion, to be passionate with somebody else.

The creative process is do-be-do-be-do. Do is what *danava* habitually engages in, but this habitual engagement will not do. For creativity, "do" means focused doing. Focusing is hard for a hyperactive, but not impossible. But "being" is even harder for the *danava* in us; the hyperactivity really hurts you here. The tendency is to do-do-do; to be is to get bored. To make room for "be" you engage with concentration meditation, focusing on an object. This slows you down; between thoughts you will now have gaps.

Better yet, do what Soto Zen practitioners teach – just sitting or *shikhan taza* in Japanese. Get bored but don't get up; that is all to the practice. Do-be-do-be-do brings quantum leaps of insight that will create a new you when manifest.

Can one build positive emotional brain circuits this way and balance the negative? You bet. There is now brain evidence of this shift to emotional intelligence. There is now understanding of what exactly is happening in the wiring of the brains to make this change. Let's call this transformed station of life the beginning of even higher intelligence.

The Transforming Task of the Deva Is Harder

Now for the *deva*. Restraining from pleasure opens us to other alternative ways to happiness – feeling, meaning, and archetypes. Engaging fundamental creativity to explore the archetypes eventually leads to the intuitive mind, a mind whose primary mode of cognition is intuition. Intuition of archetypes engages the quantum self in us; exploring the archetypes with fundamental creativity gives us longer and longer acquaintance with the quantum self. Eventually, we end up living mostly in tangled hierarchy.

When you relate to an "other" with pleasure-seeking in mind, you objectify your other. You are the head honcho of the relationship; the other's job is to please you. To make a tangled hierarchy which is a circular relationship, you need to discover the otherness of the other and respect that otherness. Restraining pleasure is a big first step to all this transformation coming your way.

There is also another problem. The creative mode of the *deva* in us is fundamental creativity. The creative process is the same do-be-do-be-do. In the "be" phase, we relax in the waking state to give unconscious processing a chance. During relaxation, the brain's tendency, and fMRI studies prove this, is to go back to the command of what neuroscientists call self-agency and what we call the ego-character-persona. So, the old ego-habits such as engagement with rational intellectualism to avoid boredom come back. Additionally, all that suppression-repression emotional stuff may also return. It is these tendencies that the *deva* has to avoid; *deva* has to clean up the personal unconscious what Jung called shadow cleansing. In archetypal terms, this is when we invite the Hindu archetype of goddess *Kali*, symbolic of the cleaning-up of the dark light, shutting part of the personal unconscious in our life.

Archetypal exploration and its successful completion begin in us a life of supramental intelligence, the culmination of higher intelligence.

Once we are open to the quantum self this way, once our ego has become authentic, free of all the inauthentic personalities that divide, the ego is ready to play with the quantum self to embody the insights gained as quantum leaps of fundamental creativity, in other words, to live in flow.

It happens. There is now neurological evidence of people living in flow.

To summarise: We establish non-locality for the *manava* in our lives mainly through the practice of meditation with others;

we need community for that. To transform the *danava* in us, we take discontinuous quantum leaps via creativity with a teacher; call her a *guru* if you like. Then as *deva*, we explore tangled hierarchy via relationship with others and eventually via flow-relationship between the two poles of our own self.

In the olden days of the discoveries that made up the Upanishads, people mostly cared about happiness, a very personal experience. By the time the *Bhagavad Gita*, *Kabbala* etc., were codified, we find additional reference to skillful action or intelligence. "*Yoga karmasu kaushalam*," yoga is skillful action, declares the *Bhagavad Gita*. Today, your personal happiness is not the only important thing, how you are able to deal with the world using your intelligence is even more important. Transformation at the *manava* level takes us from machine to human mental intelligence and also begins a re-acquaintance with feelings in the body. Transformation at the level of the *danava* is the beginning of emotional intelligence. The transformation of the *deva* matures our emotional intelligence and develops the final highest level of intelligence that is available to us human beings – supramental intelligence – the ability to deal with every situation in synchrony with the purposive movement of consciousness.

The latest neuroscience data is telling us that the brain amazingly and somewhat unexpectedly to the neuroscientists, cooperates in all this and this is part of the reason that the reports of such transformed people over the ages have become credible.

All of us must follow the examples of these transformed people who did it even without understanding much of what they were doing. Today, we have come a long way. We have a science of the brain; we have a science of transformation. Let's use this science, those of us who are getting its message. Let's transform; humanity will follow.

If you feel resistance and obstacles in your path to transformation, read Amit's book written together with Carl Blake and Gary Stuart, *Quantum Activation* and engage with some of the remedies suggested therein. As you have seen, your brain can be your biggest obstacle if you allow it to be your boss.

We finish with a story. An uneducated farmer in India was bringing a large bunch of produce from his little farm to market in the city in his oxcart. He found the road blocked by a large rock. What to do? He got down from his cart and tried and tried to remove the great rock. Little by little, the rock relented and after many hours the farmer was successful. But he was sad that he had lost a lot of time; it was too late now to go to the market. Just as he was about to turn back, he saw a bag lying where the rock was. He opened the bag and found it full of gold. There was also a letter that read, "The gold belongs to the one who has succeeded removing the rock."

Thus, every obstacle in our path including the brain is both a danger and an opportunity. The Newtonian brain is the danger; the quantum brain is opportunity.

Amen, D. (2007). *The Brain in Love.* N.Y.: Three River Press.

Aurobindo, S. (1996). *The Life Divine.* Pondicherry, India: Sri Aurobindo Ashram.

Beauregard, M. (2012). *The Spiritual Brain.*

Flanagan et al (2008). *Measuring the Immeasurable.* Boulder, CO: Sounds True.

Goleman, D. and Richardson, R. J. (2017). *Altered Traits.* NY: Penguin Random House.

Goswami, A. (1993). *The Self-Aware Universe: How Consciousness Creates the Material World.* N.Y.: Tarcher/Putnam.

Goswami, A. (2001). *Physics of the Soul.* Charlottesville, VA: Hampton Roads.

Goswami, A. (2008). *Creative Evolution.* Wheaton, IL: Theosophical Publishing House.

Goswami, A. (2014). *Quantum Creativity: Think Quantum, Be Creative.* N. Y.: Hay House.

Goswami, A. (2017). *The Everything Answer Book.* Charlottesville, VA: Hampton Roads.

Goswami, A. and Onisor, R. V. (2019). *Quantum Spirituality.* Delhi, India: Blue Star.

Goswami, A. (2021). *See the World as a Five Layered Cake.* Delhi, India: Blue Star.

Goswami, A., Blake, C.S., and Stuart, G. *Quantum Activation: transforming obstacles into Opportunities*

Goswami, A. and Pattani, S. (2021). *Quantum Psychology and Science of Happiness*. Delhi, India: Blue Star.

Hanson, R. (2009). *Buddha's Brain*. Oakland, CA: New Harbinger.

Herr, E. (2012). *Consciousness: Bridging the Gap between Conventional Science and the Super Science of Quantum Mechanics*. Faber, VA: Rainbow Ridge Books.

Kounios, J. and Beeman, M. (2015). *The Eureka Factor*. NY: Random House.

Ledoux, J. (1996). *The Emotional Brain*. N.Y.: Simon & Schuster.

Medina. J. (2008). *Brain Rules*. Seattle, WA: Pear Press.

Miller, L. (2021). *The Awakened Brain*.

Newberg, A. (2011). *How God changes your Brain*.

Nunez, P. L. (2013). *The New Science of Consciousness*. NY: Oxford University Press.

Penrose, R. (1991). *The Emperor's New Mind*. N.Y.: Penguin.

Pert, C. (1997). *Molecules of Emotion*. N.Y.: Scribner.

Radin, D. (2009). *The Noetic Universe*. London: Transworld Publishers.

Ramachandran, V. S. (2010). *The Tell-Tale Brain*. London, UK: Random House.

Searle, J. (1994). *The Rediscovery of the Mind*. Cambridge, MA: MIT Press.

Sheldrake, R. (1981). *A New Science of Life*. L.A.: Tarcher.

Stapp, H. P. (1993). *Mind, Matter, and Quantum Mechanics*.

Suzuki, W. (2015). *Healthy Brain, Happy Life*. N. Y.: Harper-Collins.

Teilhard de Chardin, P. (1961). *The Phenomenon of Man*. N.Y.: Harper & Row.

Wolff, F. M. *Philosophy of Consciousness without an Object*.

Index

A

B

C

D

E

F

G

H

I

J

K

L

M

N

O

P

Q

R

S

T

U

V

W

Y

0-9

Amit Goswami, PhD

Amit Goswami is a retired professor of physics from the University of Oregon where he served from 1968-1997. In 1985, he discovered the solution to the quantum measurement problem and developed a science of experience explicating how consciousness splits into subject and object. Subsequently, he developed a theory of reincarnation and integrated conventional and alternative medicine within the new quantum science of health. Among his discoveries are the quantum theory of the creative process, the theory of quantum evolution, the science of love and happiness, the theory of quantum economics that extends Adam's Smith's capitalism into a workable paradigm for the 21st century, and the theory of quantum spirituality based on the exploration of wholeness.

In 1999, Amit started a movement called *quantum activism*, now gaining ground in North and South America, Europe, and India. In 2018, he and his collaborators established Quantum Activism Vishwalayam, an institution of transformative education in India, based on quantum science and the primacy of consciousness.

Amit is the author of numerous books, most notably: The Self-Aware Universe, Physics of the Soul, The Quantum Doctor, God is Not Dead, Quantum Creativity, The Everything

Answer Book, Quantum Spirituality (with Valentina Onisor), Quantum Activation (with Carl Blake and Gary Stuart), and Quantum Psychology and Science of Happiness (with Sunita Pattani). He was featured in the movie What the Bleep Do We Know!? and the documentaries Dalai Lama Renaissance and The Quantum Activist.

Amit is a spiritual practitioner and calls himself a quantum activist in search of Wholeness.

Valentina R. Onisor, MD

Dr. Onisor is a practicing physician specialized in Family Medicine, who integrates various systems of alternative medicine (acupuncture, Ayurveda, naturopathy, aromatherapy) into her medical practice. Committed to consciousness awakening-related sciences for over two decades and a pioneer of quantum integrative medicine, Valentina is also a yoga and meditation teacher (Sivananda Vedanta Forest Academy; Yoga Alliance; Universal Consciousness Ambassador, CSETI). She has made correlations between the ancient sciences and quantum physics, using both as a support for her teachings. Through a unique system of quantum healing, Valentina inspires people to achieve enhanced physical, emotional, and spiritual health that allows for profound and long-lasting integration and regeneration on all levels.

As a leader in transformational education, Valentina serves as a teacher, co-founder and Dean of Students at Quantum Activism Vishwalayam, India. She is a lecturer at Quantum Academy in Brazil and an acting consultant for the Center for Quantum Activism in Eugene, OR, USA. Valentina is currently offering a number of courses and workshops oriented towards healing and spiritual transformation.

She is co-author (along with Dr. Amit Goswami) of the recently released book, *Quantum Spirituality, Quantum Brain* and of the upcoming books, *The awakening of Intelligence, The Quantum Integrative Medicine,* and *The Quantum Science of Love and Relationships*.

Made in United States
North Haven, CT
09 March 2022

16933083R00163